SHIFTING SANDS

A Study of the coast of Northern Ireland
from Magilligan to Larne

———

BELFAST : HMSO

COUNTRYSIDE AND WILDLIFE RESEARCH SERIES NO. 2

SHIFTING SANDS

A Study of the coast of Northern Ireland from Magilligan to Larne

Bill Carter

Department of Environmental Studies
University of Ulster
Coleraine
Northern Ireland
BT52 1SA

BELFAST: HMSO

© *Crown copyright 1991*
First published 1991

ISBN 0 337 08253 7

Photographs reproduced by kind permission

Cover.   Curran Strand and White Rocks, Portrush (Dr Bill Carter).

Fig. 9.   Geographical Society of Ireland, Department of Geography, St. Patrick's College, Maynooth.

Fig. 11.   Aerofilms Limited, Gate Studies, Station Road, Borehamwood, Herts, WD6 1EJ. Photograph No. A129357.

Fig. 16.   *Top.* BKS Aerial Surveys, Ballycairn Road, Coleraine. Photograph No. 2074004.
Bottom. N.I. Ordnance Survey, Department of the Environment (NI), Colby House, Stranmillis, Belfast. 1987–8203.

Fig. 31.   As 16 bottom (no number on print)

Fig. 36.   Original in Ulster Museum, Botanic Avenue, Belfast.

Fig. 42.   *Bottom photo*: E.T.W. Dennis and Sons, Limited, Melrose Street, Scarborough, N. Yorks, EY62 7SJ.

Countryside and Wildlife Research Series

A series of publications on conservation topics in Northern Ireland arising from the research and survey programme of the Countryside and Wildlife Branch.

Any views and opinions expressed in this publication are entirely those of the author and do not necessarily conform with those of the Department.

Countryside & Wildlife Branch
Department of the Environment
(Northern Ireland)
Calvert House
23 Castle Place
BELFAST
BT1 1FY

FOREWORD

Beaches and dunes have a special place in the heart. They were for many of us our first idyllic experience of the seaside as children, and they come to mind as the place to take our children on their first holiday. But our coast is much more than a playground. It is a dynamic, constantly changing frontier where the sea that covers more than two thirds of the surface of our planet meets the land that covers the remainder. The coast is never completely still. As well as the to and fro of the tide, it is a focus for human activity – industrial, residential and recreational. This narrow zone between terra firma and the great ocean is also of incomparable value to a diversity of wildlife out of all proportion to its areal extent.

We are so accustomed to the activity and the daily and seasonal cycles of the coast, that it is easy to overlook any longer term changes that may be superimposed. There are indications that some irreversible longer term factors are at work on the beaches of the north east coast. Could it be that some day our children or grandchildren will be denied the simple pleasures of a day on these magnificent beaches? It was concern that these beaches might be gradually changing that prompted the Countryside and Wildlife Branch to commission Dr. Bill Carter to study and report on this stretch of coastline. *Shifting Sands* is a condensed version of his report.

Dr Carter, from his base at the University of Ulster at Coleraine, has become widely respected as a coastal geomorphologist not only in Northern Ireland but far beyond our shores.

Our objective in the Countryside and Wildlife Branch is to safeguard the natural environment against unwelcome changes. In publishing this paper, I hope we will be stimulating appreciation of an important problem, which is in turn a necessary part of finding the solutions.

Dr. John Faulkner
Chief Scientist
Countryside and Wildlife Branch
Department of Environment (NI)

ACKNOWLEDGEMENTS

I would like to thank the many people who have helped with coastal projects in Ireland over the last 20 years. Mr. Darius Bartlett was involved in the 1987–1988 DoE(NI) survey which formed the basis of this book, and I would like to record my appreciation of his interest and effort. In addition, the Countryside and Wildlife Branch of the DoE(N.I.), especially Dr. Andrew Stott and Mr. Richard Weyl provided constant encouragement and were kind enough to read and comment on the original draft manuscript. I thank you gentlemen.

My support staff in the University of Ulster, have as always, been superb. Mrs. Mary McCamphill, Mr. Kilian McDaid and Mr. Nigel McDowell have put an enormous amount of hard work into dealing with my requests, usually to unacceptable deadlines. I owe them a great debt of gratitude.

Dr. Bill Carter
Coleraine

CONTENTS

___

Foreword v

Acknowledgement vi

List of figures viii

Introduction 1

Area of Study 3

The Natural Environment 4

The Coastal Sites 10

   Magilligan 10

   Castlerock and Portstewart 12

   The mouth of the River Bann 15

   Portstewart and Portrush 16

   Portrush - the West Bay 16

   Portrush - the East Strand 18

   White Rocks to Portballintrae 20

   Portballintrae 21

   Runkerry (Bushfoot Strand) 24

Giant's Causway Cliffs 24

White Park Bay 28

Ballintoy Harbour and Boheeshane Bay 29

Rathlin Island 30

Ballycastle 30

Ballycastle to Cushendun 33

Cushendun 34

Cushendall 36

Red Bay and Waterfoot 37

Red Bay to Carnlough 38

Carnlough and Glenarm 40

Glenarm to Larne 42

Future Management 44

Bibliography 46

References 47

Index 49

LIST OF FIGURES

Page No.

1. Map of the northeast coast of Northern Ireland. 2
2. The essential geology of the North Coast is well seen in this quarry near the White Rocks at Portrush. 4
3. The sea-level curve for northeast Ireland. 5
4. The recent tide gauge record from Malin Head. 5
5. This photograph of Portstewart shows long swell waves with shorter sea on top. 7
6. Schematic view of a rip current flowing seaward from the beach. 7
7. A 5-minute wave trace from Portrush during the storm of 14 January 1986. 8
8. Magilligan is about 6,500 years old and comprises a series of over 250 east/west beach ridges. 10
9. Erosion of the Magilligan foreland. 11
10. The foredune ridges at Magilligan Point form anecological succession. 12
11. The Castlerock dune complex. 13
12. Dune damage near the beach access at Portstewart. 14
13. Changing areas of bare sand at the east end of Portstewart Strand. 14
14. A 1930s photograph of Portstewart Strand. 15
15. The Bann mouth is confined to a deep channel by two parallel jetties. 16
16. The shrinking beach at Portrush may be seen in these views taken over the last 90 years. 17
17. Coastal changes at Portrush. 18
18. The high level of dune degradation at Portrush is due partly to the large number of visitors. 19
19. The dune cliff faces at Portrush show numerous signs of failure. 20
20. The chalk cliffs near the White Rocks show a 'double' slope profile. 20
21. The once sandy beach at Portballintrae has disappeared leaving a gravel shoreline. 21
22 The small pier near Seaport Lodge at Portballintrae. 22
23. The first attempts to stabilise the cliff slope at Portballintrae failed. 22
24. A schematic plan of Portballintrae bay showing the sediment grading along the shore. 23
25. Viewed from the air it is easy to spot the wide crescentic bars that dominate the bay at Runkerry. 24

26. The Causeway cliffs are among Europe's most spectacular coastlines. 25
27. About 20,000 years ago the Causeway probably looked like this. 26
28. The collapse of the Giant's Eye Glass in 1949 is one major change that has occurred. 26
29. The gradual disappearance of blocks on the Giant's Causeway. 27
30. Near Dunseverick there is abundant evidence of raised beach forms. 28
31. A vertical air photograph of White Park Bay. 29
32. The tidal 'sundial' (left) on the Church of Ireland at Ballintoy. 30
33. Boheeshane Bay includes some of the best rockfall features in Ireland. 31
34. The sediment that forms Ballycastle Beach almost certainly derives from the Carey Valley and Glenshesk. 31
35. Ballycastle Beach comprises a microtidal gravel beach fronted by a flat, sandy, subtidal zone. 32
36. An old painting c.1828 by Andrew Nichol of the eastern end of Ballycastle Beach 32
37. Erosion forms on the shoreline near Pans Rocks at Ballycastle. 33
38. The rock talus cliffs of Fair Head. 34
39. The probable movement of sediment in Cushendun Bay. 35
40. Coastline recession at Cushendun since 1960. 35
41. Changes to the beach at Cushendall. 36
42. Photographs show the retreat of the shoreline at Cushendall. 37
43. Major rotational landslips of the Antrim Coast. 38
44. Minor slope instabilities are clearly visible along much of the coast. 39
45. The likely environmental impact of the Antrim Coast Road on the sediment budget. 39
46. Earlier this century the seawall at Carnlough was fronted by a substantial gravel beach. 40
47. The seawall at Carnlough is in a very poor state of repair. 41
48. Sediment removal from the beach at Glenarm. 41
49. The coast at Ballygalley shows a low sea wall and depleted beach levels. 42
50. The Curran photographed in the late 19th Century. 43
51. A diagrammatic view of the gravel ridge development at Larne. 43

INTRODUCTION

This volume is derived from a number of studies of the coast of Northern Ireland over the last 25 years. In particular, much of the information was gathered as part of a Department of the Environment funded project at the University of Ulster from 1987 to 1988. The subsequent technical Report (Carter and Bartlett, 1988) was not circulated widely, despite considerable local interest. It is the aim of this publication to present the earlier Report in a more amenable form for the public and to provide background information on the way in which the coastline of Northeast Ireland is changing.

The population of Northern Ireland is lucky in having easy access to what is arguably one of the world's most scenic coastlines. Visitors, from far and near, cannot fail to be impressed with the magnificent scenery of the Causeway Coast or the splendour of the Antrim Glens where they sweep down to the shore. For well over a century this scenic resource has been exploited, boosting a predominantly agricultural economy with tourism, so that many communities (for example, Ballycastle, Cushendall) have a dual function, serving both farmers and visitors, while others (Portrush, Portstewart) are primarily seaside resorts. The role of the coast is central to tourism, providing beaches, dunes and inshore waters for all manner of formal and informal activities. Despite the impact of 'The Troubles' on tourism (Pollard 1989), the shoreline has come under increasing pressure, particularly from the domestic market. This is epitomised by the enormous growth in the number of caravans (Carter, 1982a), used mainly as 'second-homes', the increasing restaurant and hotel trade, the development of marinas, interpretation centres, golf courses and many other leisure-based activities. At many locations there is active competition between developers for shoreline resources. It would be fallacious to infer that only tourism was important. The coast supports agriculture on reclaimed land, inshore fisheries, military and civil firing ranges, commercial harbours and quays as well as being used for waste disposal, aggregate mining and power generation.

All these activities occur in a zone well-known for its natural propensity to change. When confronted by change, the traditional response has been to build sea defences to withstand attack by the sea. Over the years much of the non-rocky coast of Northern Ireland has been 'protected' in one way or another, so that very little of today's coast may be said to be natural except for the cliffs.

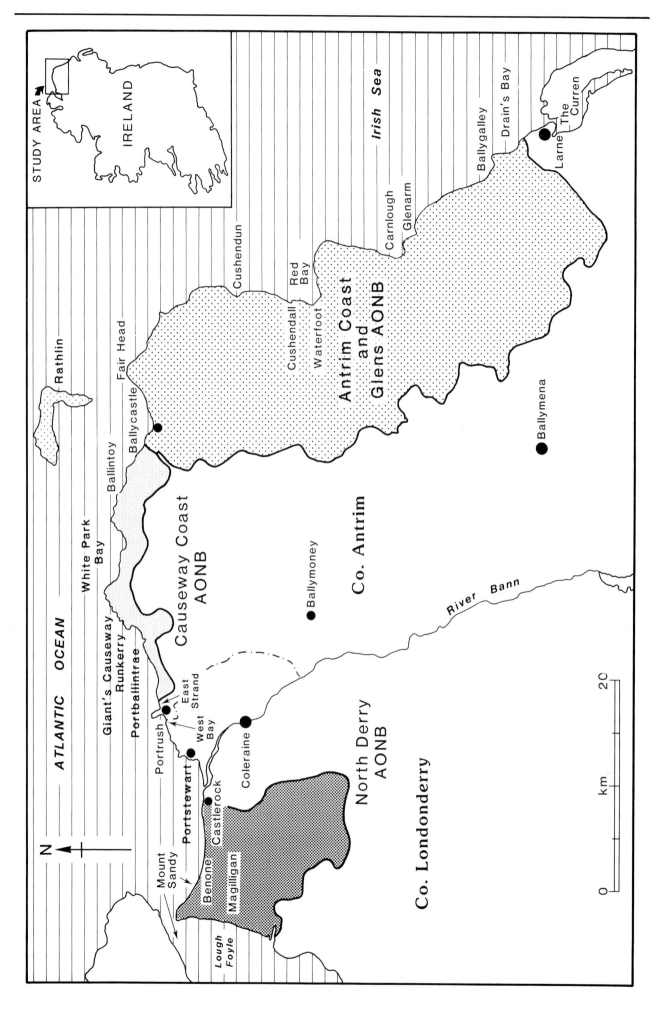

STUDY AREA

IRELAND

ATLANTIC OCEAN

Rathlin

Fair Head

White Park Bay

Ballintoy

Ballycastle

Giant's Causeway

Runkerry

Portballintrae

Portrush

East Strand

West Bay

Portstewart

Mount Sandy

Benone

Castlerock

Magilligan

Lough Foyle

Causeway Coast AONB

Cushendun

Red Bay

Cushendall

Waterfoot

Antrim Coast and Glens AONB

Irish Sea

Ballygalley

Drain's Bay

Carnlough

Glenarm

Larne

The Curren

Ballymena

Co. Antrim

Ballymoney

River Bann

North Derry AONB

Coleraine

Co. Londonderry

N

km

0   20

AREA OF STUDY

The study area extends from Magilligan Point at the mouth of Lough Foyle (Irish Grid Reference C6539) to The Curran at Larne (D4101) a distance of approximately 227km (including Rathlin Island) (Fig.1). Included in this stretch of shoreline are no less than three designated Areas of Outstanding Natural Beauty (AONBs) – the North Derry, the Causeway Coast and the Antrim Coast and Glens, which between them embrace about 30% of the highest quality scenic coast in Ireland (Carter, 1987). Given the intrinsic beauty of the coast, it is Government policy that it shall be safeguarded from unsightly and unessential development. Much of the shoreline and the adjacent land is owned privately. Among the largest landowners are the National Trust, who since 1933 have acquired long stretches of the coast of Northern Ireland, including important sites like the Giants Causeway, White Park Bay, Murlough Bay and Portstewart. Ownership of the land below the High Water Mark (HWM) is often disputed, although most is controlled by either the Crown Estate Commissioners (a Government agency vested with the management of the sea bed) or The Honourable, The Irish Society (a residuary body which oversees the remaining interests of the London Companies). Access to the coast is relatively easy, as the main coast road (A2) parallels much of the shore, and there are numerous parking places along the way. Elsewhere, long distance footpaths allow penetration of all but the most inaccessible sites. Although it is possible to reach all of the beaches, some are more popular than others. Portstewart Beach – on which you may park your car – may attract over 5000 visitors on a fine summer's day (Carter, 1987), while at White Park Bay (which is a kilometre from the nearest car park) it is rare to encounter more than a few dozen people at a time. The Giant's Causeway is perhaps the most-visited natural curiosity in Ireland. The unusual – but by no means unique – arrangement of columnar basalt attracts over a quarter of a million visitors every year. The Causeway has a long pedigree as a tourist attraction, visitors were drawn to it as early as the late 1600s.

1. Map of the northeast coast of Northern Ireland showing the locations of AONBs and places mentioned in the text.

3

THE NATURAL ENVIRONMENT

Geology

Much of the coast is formed of late-Mesozoic (65 to 130 million years ago (Ma)) and Tertiary (25 to 65 Ma) rocks, overlain by a veneer of more recent (last 40,000 years) glacial deposits. Almost the entire study area falls within the so-called Thulian Volcanic Province of northeast Europe associated with the initial tectonic rifting of the North Atlantic between 53 and 65 Ma (Preston, 1981). As the Earth's crust extended, basaltic lava flowed out across a karstic plain formed of White Limestone (chalk). The relationship between the two rock types is well exposed at Craig-a-hula Quarry near Portrush (Fig. 2). Much of the coastal framework has been determined by faulting and volcanic intrusions (dykes and sills) within these two major rock types. More often than not major faults, like the Port Bradden fault which runs from Port Ballintoy Harbour to Portrush, control the configuration of the coast.

During the last 2 million years, Northern Ireland was subject to repeated glaciations. In most cases ice moved south onto the coast from Scotland, although local ice from the Bann Valley and smaller centres in the Glens of Antrim and the Sperrins may have moved north, crossing the coast. The final ice incursion – the late-Midlandian stage – which lasted from about 30,000 to 17,000 years before present – has played a major role in shaping the present day coast. Two factors are especially important; first the ice brought vast quantities of sediment and dumped it in and around the present coast; and second, the weight of the ice on the local rocks caused isostatic subsidence of perhaps 150 to 200m (Bowen, 1978). After the ice sheet melted (or retreated) the land began to rise slowly. About 20,000 years ago the North Channel between Scotland and Ireland would have been filled with an ice sheet. It is likely the ice extended into the Bann Valley and the Antrim Glens. Under the ice, the sea may have reached well inland from the present coast. Many of the glacial

2. *The essential geology of the North Coast is well seen in this photograph of a quarry near the White Rocks at Portrush. The volcanic basalt has flowed out across a chalk surface, infilling depressions and caves.*

deposits of northeast Ireland are now interpreted as glaciomarine (Eyles and McCabe, 1989), that is they were lain down under sea ice.

Sea-level history

If we are to understand how our coast evolved then it is important to know how sea level has changed. We have already mentioned how ice pushes the land down, with the result that relative sea level rises. Conversely as the ice melts, the land rises and sea level falls. Unfortunately this very simple model is complicated by the fact that as an ice sheet forms, water is withdrawn from the oceans so sea level falls and as the ice melts water rejoins the ocean and sea level rises. Thus the position of sea-level at any one time represents a balance between isostatic (crustal loading) and eustatic (ocean level) factors. The north of Ireland has had a particularly complex sea-level history (Carter, 1982b, Carter et al., 1989) with the water levels rising and falling several times over the last 20,000 years (Fig. 3).

Towards the end of the ice age, sea level appears to have been relatively high. McCabe and Eyles (1988) believe that the deltas in the upper Carey Valley near Ballycastle at heights of 50 to 70 metres above present Ordnance Datum are of marine origin, forming where glacial streams reached the sea. Other evidence of high sea levels is found on the Inishowen Peninsula in Donegal where raised beaches up to 20m in height are found (Stephens and Synge, 1965).

As the ice retreated, sea level fell rapidly, and by 13,000 years ago probably stood at 30 to 40m below the present level. At this time, most of the North Channel would have been land and it is likely Ireland and Scotland were connected (Devoy, 1985). Gradually as the world's oceans refilled, sea level rose again. As it did, the glacial sediments left in the region of the North Channel were reworked and moved landward, eventually accumulating along our present coast. Around 9,000 years ago sea level rose quickly flooding coastal lagoons near the present Bann Mouth and a peat bog near Carnlough. In the north of Ireland, sea level was slightly above its present level between 4,500 and 6,500 years ago. The sea flooded the estuaries of the Foyle, Bann and probably flooded the lower reaches of the Glens, although these narrow valleys may have been blocked by huge gravel barriers so that the water never penetrated too far inland. At this period – known as the mid-Holocene – most of our coastal scenery began to form. The sand dunes at Portrush, Portstewart and Castlerock all date from about 5,000 years ago, while the beach ridge plain of Magilligan would have been extending rapidly northward. After 4,500 BP the sea-level fell away slightly, abandoning a narrow raised beach along the whole coast (Fig. 4). This period almost certainly marks the last major influx of marine sediment to the shoreline.

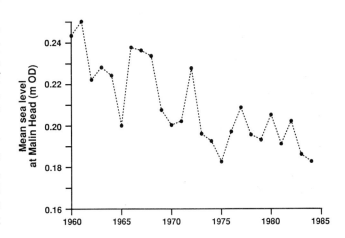

4. The recent tide gauge record from Malin Head shows a persistent sea level fall since it was installed in 1960.

The course of sea-level over the last 2,000 years is not well-known. Most likely it has remained within a metre or so of the present level. There is some evidence that the isostatic recovery of Ireland is not complete; at Malin Head a tide gauge established in 1960 shows an almost continuous fall averaging 2mm/year over the last 25 years (Fig. 4). Further south, the tide record in Belfast Harbour shows a similar trend, although here the gradual reclaiming of land in Belfast Lough may be distorting the record (Carter 1982c). There is a distinct probability that world sea-levels will rise by 0.5 to 1.0m in the next century, although the exact amount will vary from place to place. Northern Ireland as a whole is well-sited, and it is unlikely that there will be any noticeable increase in sea level before 2020 AD and substantial impact will probably not occur until the second half of the twenty-first millenium.

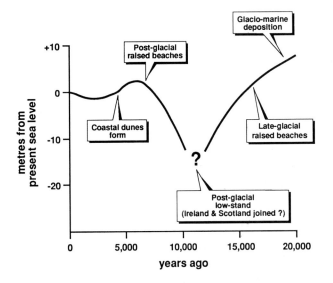

3. The sea-level curve for northeast Ireland, showing the approximate periods when our coastal scenery formed.

Coastal types and sediments

The coastline of northeast Ireland comprises rocky headlands and cliffs interspersed with boulder, gravel or sand beaches. A number of extensive dune systems occur, and, in places, the shoreline is cut by river mouths and estuaries, the largest of which is Lough Foyle (155km²). A summary of shoreline types is given in Table 1.

Table 1. Shoreline types

Shore type	Length km	%
Rock and earth cliffs	48.8	21.5
Rock platforms	35.9	15.9
Sandy beaches	29.7	13.1
Rock, boulder or gravel beaches	48.1	21.3
Artificial coasts (seawalls etc.)	52.1	22.9
Estuary/river mouth	12.1	5.3
Total	226.7	100.00

Coastal sediments derive from three main sources: first, much of the material has come from the seabed. During the Holocene (last 10,000 years), sea-level rise material was swept-up and accumulated along the coast. Much of this material is glacial in origin, comprising numerous boulders and pebbles from afar, mainly western Scotland. The finer material is predominantly quartz, mixed with a small quantity of heavy minerals, including garnets, tourmaline and olivene. The seabed also supplies small quantities of carbonate sand, largely from broken shells. This carbonate material is constantly recycled and adds nothing to the long term sediment budget. Second, sediment has been supplied by rivers. The beaches east and south of Ballycastle, with the exception of Waterfoot, are composed largely of river-borne sands and gravels, which have been reworked by the sea. The supply of river sediment was probably at a maximum in the early post-glacial (c.15,000 years ago) declining thereafter. Today the man-made modification of many of our water courses has greatly reduced rivers as a source of beach material.

Third, sediment is eroded directly by the sea from cliffs and platforms. This source is locally important along the basalt coastline between Portstewart and the Causeway Cliffs, where there are many pocket beaches formed of angular and sub-rounded basalt blocks that have been quarried from the shore platforms or fallen from the cliffs. Prior to the construction of the Antrim coast road in the 1830s, it appears likely that much of the coast south of Carnlough was intermittently supplied by rockfalls and slides, and that, in time, this material was transported south to feed many small bays, such as Glenarm and Ballygalley. Nowadays much of this supply is impeded by the road and various shore protection structures.

Size analysis of the beach sediments shows that, in almost every case, the material is distinctive at each site (Table 2). Only at Castlerock and Portstewart, which in any case are separated only by the River Bann, are the sediments similar. This strongly refutes the commonly expressed idea that the beaches are supplied by 'longshore drift', for if they were we might expect them all to show similarities in terms of size and sorting. Furthermore, the beaches in the West Bay at Portrush and Portballintrae are graded, with the sediment varying from coarse to fine along the shore. Size grading develops as a means of balancing wave processes against beach form. It only occurs when there is a lack of sediment being transported along the shoreline, and as such is an indication of shoreline maturity.

Table 2. Sediment data for some northeast coast beaches

	Mean size mm	Range of sizes mm	Sorting	Grading
Magilligan				
– Lough Foyle	0.18	0.17–0.24	Good	No
– Point	0.19	0.16–0.27	Moderate	Yes
– Benone	0.18	0.15–0.21	Very good	No
Castlerock	0.17	0.16–0.18	Very good	No
Portstewart	0.17	0.16–0.19	Very good	No
Portrush				
– West Bay	0.24	0.20–0.41	Moderate	Yes
– East Strand	0.23	0.19–0.25	Good	No
Portballintrae	0.16	0.14–0.20[1]	Poor	Yes
	150.00	0.50–600.0[2]	Poor	No
Runkerry (Bushfoot)	0.33	0.30–0.37	Poor	No
White Park Bay	0.27	0.20–0.28	Good	No
Ballycastle	0.25	0.19–4.11	Moderate	No
Cushendun	0.32	0.18–0.40	Moderate	No
Cushendall	0.57	0.20–0.65[1]	Poor	
	35.00	10.00–60.00[2]	Poor	No

Waves, tides and river flows

The coastline of northeast Ireland is subject to constant attack by waves. The relative effectiveness of the waves is controlled, in part, by longer-term variations in water level, which may be of two types: firstly, a regular rise and fall of tide, associated with the phases of the sun and moon, and secondly, irregular changes in water level due to meteorological conditions. These are called surges and in exceptional cases, may exceed a metre or more. Two types of wave are commonly encountered, swell and sea (Fig. 5). Swell is product of distant storms, and by the time the waves reach

5. *Sea and swell waves are usually distinguished in terms of length and height. This photograph of Portstewart shows long swell waves with shorter sea on top. The swell waves may have travelled thousands of kilometres, while the sea is generated by local winds.*

Ireland they may have travelled several thousand kilometres. Swell waves are often 150–300m in length (wave periods of 10–14 seconds) and as they approach the shore they build up, perhaps reaching two or more metres in height before breaking, usually parallel to the beach, to form surf. The beaches between Magilligan and Ballycastle are dominated by swell, with the highest waves occurring along the length of Runkerry (Bushfoot) Strand. Beyond Ballycastle the swell declines in size, yet it is still important. Atlantic swell penetrates the Irish Sea at least as far south as Co. Down.

Locally, sea waves are equally important. Sea waves are formed directly as wind blows over water. Usually they are shorter and approach the shoreline at an angle. Sea waves assume far more importance in sheltered areas like Lough Foyle, behind the Skerries at Portrush, or south and east of Ballycastle along the Antrim coast.

The beaches of northeast Ireland are constantly changing as the waves vary from day to day. The beach tries to reach an accommodation with the waves, but it is usually lagging just behind. It is important to understand how the beaches are 'organised' to lessen the effects of the approaching waves – many of which are more powerful than heavy lorries at full speed. On the swell-dominated coast – Magilligan to Ballycastle – the waves often break and reform several times before they reach the shoreline. As the breaking occurs the waves generate currents which flow inside the surf zone, occasionally moving seaward as rips (Fig. 6). Beneath the waves sand bars form, often in the

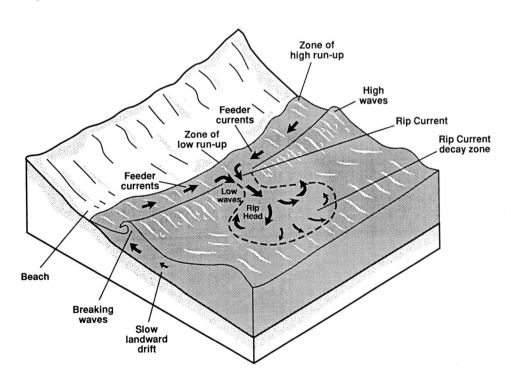

6. *Schematic view of a rip current flowing seaward from the beach. Note the longshore feeder currents, and the way the rip current dissipates outside the breaker zone.*

Zone of high run-up

High waves

Feeder currents

Rip Current

Zone of low run-up

Rip Current decay zone

Feeder currents

Low waves

Rip Head

Beach

Breaking waves

Slow landward drift

shape of crescents pointing landward. The seaward-moving rips pass between the bars and die-out beyond the waves. On most of our North Coast beaches the rip currents are spaced at regular intervals along the shore, usually between 300 and 500 metres apart. The biggest rips often occur near rocks at the ends of the bays. Rip currents are very dangerous and every year people get into danger as they are swept seaward, not knowing that to escape they should swim sideways instead of against the current. At Runkerry, White Park Bay and Ballycastle the crescentric bars are smaller, often only 60–150m wide, and may be due to resonant waves generated between headlands (Carter and Kitcher, 1979; Shaw, 1985).

Where the waves approach the coast at an angle a longshore current is formed. Longshore currents rarely have velocities of more than a few centimetres a second, but they are important in transporting sediment thrown up by the waves. Longshore currents are present all along the east coast of Ireland and are responsible for moving considerable amounts of sediments into bays and estuaries. Some of the most vigorous longshore currents may be found at Magilligan Point (Carter, 1980) or along the Antrim Coast road south of Garron Point, although in the latter case there is very little sediment capable of being moved.

During periods of strong onshore winds, the sea surface may rise abnormally high. At Portrush any water level over 2.0m O.D. is likely to be associated with a storm surge. At such times, the waves may attack the backshore and erosion can occur. Often erosion is part of an attempt to balance-out the sediment budget across the shore, counteracting high levels of wave energy. Sand, like money in a bank account, is 'withdrawn' from the dunes or the upper beach, to build up (= to spend) the lower shore profile so that it can withstand and control the larger waves. In time this loan is repaid, with sand being transferred back onto the upper beach or into the dunes. This cycle of events takes between 30 and 120 days at Magilligan (Carter, 1986), and slightly shorter elsewhere. It is important to realise that our beaches are in a constant state of flux and that we should not be too alarmed when we experience periods of rapid erosion, particularly on the swell-dominated coasts, as such periods simply form part of the long-term exchange of material between the beach, the dune and the nearshore zone. Furthermore occasional storms are very important to the coastal ecology as they help fertilise large areas by stirring-up and transporting nutrients so improving biological productivity.

Mean wave height varies around the coast (Table 3). The highest one percent of waves will be about two times the mean height, with extreme waves reaching 8 to 10m inshore. Figure 7 is a trace of the waves recorded at Portrush during the height of the storm of 14 January 1986. Such huge waves are very unusual, and if they do occur they may cause considerable damage.

Tides on the north coast are semi-diurnal (high water occurs every 12 hours 25 minutes). Spring tidal

Table 3. Wave heights in metres

	Average	Maximum[1]
N. Atlantic (off Scotland)	2.15	3.40
Magilligan	0.85	1.44
Portrush	0.72	1.22
Ballycastle	0.40	0.65
Larne (Whitehead)	0.28	0.52

[1]Maximum wave height refers to the mean value of the highest 1% of all waves.

Table 4. Spring tidal ranges in metres

Lough Foyle (Magilligan)	2.3
Portrush	1.7
Ballycastle	0.8
Cushendun	1.8
Waterfoot	2.0
Larne	2.8

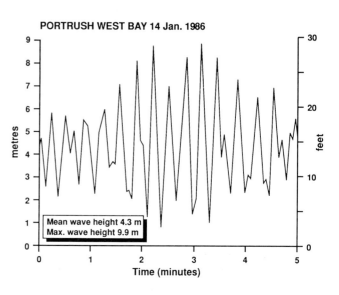

7. *A 5-minute wave trace from Portrush during the storm of 14 January 1986. These are among the highest waves and largest periods ever recorded at this site.*

range varies along the shore (Table 4) from around 1.5m at Ballycastle to 2.8m at Magilligan and Larne. 'Spring' is the old English word for 'rising', and is unconnected with the seasons. The tidal streams generally flow west to east as the tide floods reversing as the tide ebbs, although many of the embayments see a circulatory clockwise motion during the flood. Except at the estuary mouths tidal currents are very low. Approximately 440 x 10³ m³ flows in and out of Lough Foyle and 150 x 10³ m³ in and out of the Bann every tide. The interaction of waves and tides is important in 'stirring' the sea and sustains much of the sub-tidal flora and fauna by providing nutrients for growth.

Currents generated by rivers flowing out to sea are locally important. Very often the fresh water is a dark colour due to the presence of peat, and can be traced some distance, perhaps kilometres, offshore as it spreads out from the river mouth. The surface boundary between the fresh and salt water may be marked by a line of foam and a distinct colour change. Such patterns are often visible at the mouths of the Bann, Bush or Margy. The river currents are important because not only do they alter the incoming waves, bending them in towards the strongest flow, but also they create longshore currents by drawing nearshore water towards the river mouth. In time, sediments will accumulate within these convergent current zones, forming delta-like forms of marine sediment. In some instances, variations in river and wave energy lead to the continual shifting of the river mouth deltas (shoals) making them hazardous for navigation. For example, the River Bann has a long history of navigation problems, which have never been solved satisfactorily (see page 15).

The river mouths are zones of intense mixing. The interaction of waves, tides and freshwater flows result in the constant circulation of water and sediment. The widespread artificial alteration of our rivers by drainage, abstraction and flow regulation has led to the suppression of peak floods and as a consequence changes at the river mouths. The reclamation of land in the Foyle Estuary may have had a similar effect, leading to a diminution of flood at the estuary mouth.

Coastal Management

Over the last 20 years there has been a growing awareness that coastal resources are valuable and need to be managed, if they are to retain their quality and usefulness. Management is essentially foresight, and takes many forms from preservation of rare plants and animals to controlling crowds on summer Sundays. Largely because of this range, there has been a trend towards 'integrated' management, that is the formulation and execution of plans which try to balance a number of objectives over a specified period of time (usually a year). A useful approach is to 'zone' the coast for a variety of different uses, segregating conflicting activities (e.g. bird watching and power boating) as far as possible. Zoning may also be used for hazard management, perhaps identifying areas at risk from flooding or oil spills, and as part of planning and development control.

In Northern Ireland, coastal management derives from a number of sources. The Government, especially the Department of the Environment, (DOE (NI)) is responsible for developing and integrating the management framework. This has involved the designation of Areas of Special Control (ASCs) for planning purposes, Areas of Outstanding Natural Beauty (AONBs) for conservation and amenity purposes, as well as Nature Reserves and Areas of Special Scientific Interest (ASSIs) for protecting rare or threatened habitats or species or important scientific and educational sites. The DOE (NI) has a team of wardens involved in day to day management of these areas.

At local levels the District Councils provide management, particularly for coastal recreation. This may involve purpose-built facilities like the Benone Tourist Complex near Limavady, or just lay-bys and picnic tables at viewpoints.

Between Downhill and Cushendun, the National Trust own much of the coastal strip, including the Causeway Cliffs and the Giant's Causeway. The Trust has been active in managing their coastal properties, particularly through the improvement of facilities and the provision of information. Some very badly despoiled sites, like Larrybane Quarry, have been restored for amenity purposes, while other more sensitive areas, for example the Bann Estuary and Murlough Bay have been subject to more subtle management, aimed at retaining a wilder, more secluded, environment.

There are a number of coastal issues to be faced along the shore. These include the problems of access, erosion, pollution, sand mining and habitat destruction. Many of these problems are linked together, and occur at several sites. Moreover the problems may vary according to perception. For example those people wishing to launch boats may complain about lack of access to the shore, while others may believe that too much access is disturbing the wildlife. Management is there to solve such problems.

Coastal managers are rarely free to make balanced decisions, all too often they are drawn into insoluble conflicts. The expansion of golf courses into coastal dunes raises concerns about the survival of rare orchids; the requested planning permission for salmon farm cages has an impact on the traditional fishing industry. These sorts of issues are multiplying, especially as more and more people visit or even come to live by the sea. The coast from Magilligan to Larne is a precious resource. Only with effective, co-ordinated management can it stay that way.

THE COASTAL SITES

This section will examine the coastal sites from Magilligan to the Curran at Larne, focussing on their recent history of coastal changes.

Magilligan

The coastal foreland of Magilligan (Fig. 8) is one of the largest depositional shoreline features in the British Isles. Along with Dungeness in southeast England, Magilligan is one of two depositional landforms visible on the TV weather map. The geological history of Magilligan is very recent, having evolved over the last 5000 years as sea level fell from a local post-glacial high of about 5m O.D. (Carter, 1982b; Wilson and Farrington, 1989). As the sea fell so a staircase of SE-NW sand beach ridges formed, about 250 to 300 in total. In places the beach sand was blown into low dune ridges, separated by wet interdune (slacks) in which lagoons and fen peats formed.

As Magilligan grew towards the north, so it was eroded on the west by sea waves generated within Lough Foyle. Eventually, the ridge building came to an end, probably because sea level stabilised (perhaps slightly below its present level) and the sediment feed

8. *Magilligan is about 6,500 years old and comprises a series of over 250 east/west beach ridges which developed as the sea level fell and material was moved ashore from the shelf.*

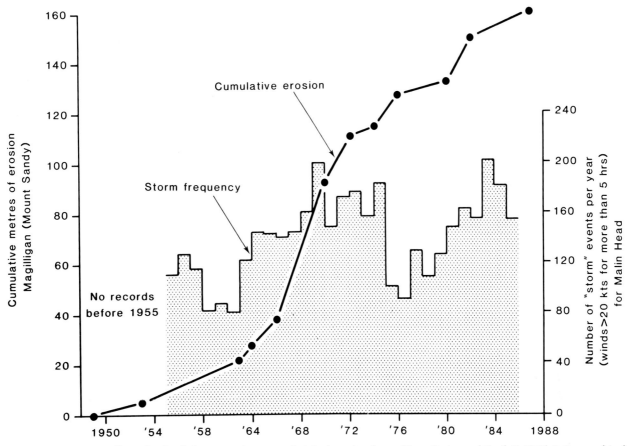

9. *Erosion of the Magilligan foreland since 1949 has exceeded 3m/year in places. (from Carter and Bartlett 1990) © Geographical Society of Ireland.*

from the shelf ceased. Whatever the exact cause, the northwest shoreline began to recede, and large quantities of sand were released to form the high dunes (up to 18m OD) that we find along the present shoreline.

The fastest shoreline erosion in Northern Ireland today is taking place near Mount Sandy on the Magilligan Foreland. Rates of over 3m/year are commonplace, and since the first aerial photographs in 1949, some parts of the shoreline have receded by over 160m (Fig. 9). This was not always the case; examination of sequences of maps since the eighteenth century suggests that the shoreline has advanced and retreated at various times. Carter *et al.* (1982) attempted to reconstruct the wave conditions that may have existed in 1882 and 1941 using a computer simulation. The results indicated that the shape and size of the offshore shoal – the Tuns Bank – were crucial in determining whether or not the Magilligan shoreline would erode. It was clear that as the shoal expanded so erosion prevailed at the shore. Conversely as the shoal contracted then the shoreline accreted. The link between the shoal and the shore is provided by the degree of wave refraction (or bending). Over shorter periods of time, it appears that variations in erosion are related to climatic change, particularly wind direction, which together with refraction, concentrates

wave energy and erosion at some places along the beach. Thus viewed from afar, Magilligan appears to be crooked, with a meandering shoreline.

The sand hills at Magilligan may be eroded very quickly during periods of high waves, high tides and onshore winds. The dune cliffs repeatedly collapse and sand is dispersed offshore, accumulating in broad sand bars parallel to the beach. Some sediment returns to the beach, but several tens of thousands cubic metres move to the north and west, eventually re-emerging from the water as a new beach ridge near the Point. Here, over 250 metres of new dune ridges have formed since 1953 (Carter and Wilson, 1990). The development of new foredunes is a rare event in the British Isles, and although the Magilligan examples are the result of 'canabalisation' of older dunes, they nonetheless provide an important ecological and educational resource.

The dunes at Magilligan Point (Fig. 10) show a typical environmental succession. Within a few years the soil changes from base-rich to acid-rich, as the carbonate content drops and the proportion of organic material rises (Wilson, 1987). The vegetation changes from sand fixers and binders like Sea Couch-grass (*Elymus farctus*) and Marram (*Ammophila arenaria*) to sand stabilisers like Fescues (*Festuca rubra, F.*

1963　　1966　　1968

10. *The foredune ridges at Magilligan Point form an ecological succession. These ridges advanced seaward over a period of 15 years (1953–1968). A full description is contained in Carter and Wilson (1990).*

ovina), Bird's-foot Trefoil (*Lotus corniculatus*) as well as various mosses. Given time, the succession may mature towards acidiophilus grassland, perhaps dominated by the Burnet Rose (*Rosa pimpinellifolia*), Bracken (*Pteridium aquilinum*) or heathland.

Magilligan Point has extended by c. 75ha in recent years. This outgrowth may be related to the gradual loss of water volume within Lough Foyle, through a combination of natural siltation and land reclamation. However, contrary to local opinion it is unlikely that Magilligan will one day extend across to Inishowen; there will always be a channel kept open. The Point plays an important role in determining sedimentation patterns in Lough Foyle. Sediment is transported towards the Point both from the Lough Foyle shore and the Atlantic beaches. The wave transport gradient declines sharply towards the Point, making it a zone of net accumulation. Some of this material, as we have seen, is blown into the dunes, but a substantial proportion is dispersed into the estuary channel and finally comes to rest in the sand shoals inside or outside the estuary.

Magilligan must be viewed as a slowly evolving coastal system, within which the beach, dunes and offshore shoals all play important parts. Moving east the rate of change falls dramatically, so that the coast from Benone to Castlerock is one of the most stable shorelines in Northern Ireland. Over the last 150 years the shoreline has neither advanced nor retreated, and it is only rarely that the storm waves scarp the dune edge.

Castlerock and Portstewart

It is useful to consider the two beaches east and west of the Bann Estuary as a single unit. Both are very flat, fine grained, high energy shorelines, ideal for surfing. Over a year, the beach level usually rises and falls by less than a metre. The stability of the beaches means that the dunes are threatened only rarely by wave erosion, and on those occasions when it does occur, the sand is rapidly returned from whence it came.

Both beaches are backed by extensive dunes, although many of the more natural features at Castlerock (Fig. 11) have been replaced by golf fairways, tees and greens. However, just to the south of Castlerock, near to where the Articlave River enters the estuary, a layer of ancient oak leaves were found embedded in the dune sands (Hamilton and Carter, 1985). These gave a ^{14}C date of 5350 years before present (BP), the earliest date for coastal dunes in Ireland.

At first sight the Portstewart dunes appear less affected by man, but this probably belies the truth. From the air the dune system shows a series of transverse ridges at right angles to the coast, with bare sand covering many windward slopes. The dunes are about 5000 years old, but have undergone many changes since then. The first dunes were perched on the gravel ridge pushed onshore as the sea rose to its post-glacial maximum. The gravel may still be seen in places flooring the dune depressions or blowouts. Close inspection reveals that the gravels contain many sea shells, some now locally extinct (McMillan, 1935). Human disturbance of the dunes as well as the actions of storms has led major physiographic changes. The modern dunes are well vegetated, and support a number of rarer plants like orchids. The widespread planting of Sea Buckthorn (*Hippophae rhamnoides*) has proved a mixed blessing. On one hand, the dense, spikey bushes have deterred access and undoubtably reduced erosion, but on the other the buckthorn has invaded and replaced the natural dune grassland and lowered the plant species diversity of the area. The plant has spread dramatically since being planted in the 1930s and now covers 19.5 ha. One group of beneficiaries have been small birds, which find shelter and food in the buckthorn thickets.

The spread of Sea Buckthorn is only one of several management problems at Portstewart. Perhaps the most worrying is the loss of vegetation cover associ-

11. The Portstewart and
Castlerock dunes began forming
c. 5,000 years ago as sea level
began to fall on the north coast of
Ireland. This photograph shows
the Castlerock dune complex.

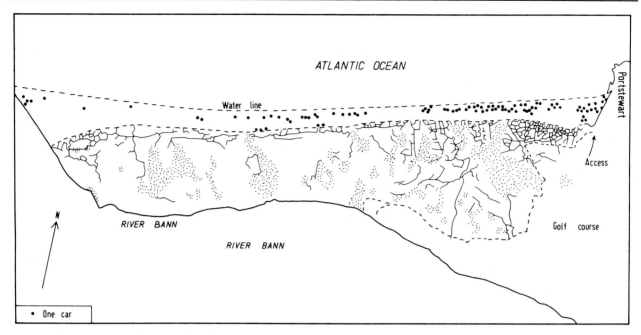

12. *Dune damage indicated near the beach access at Portstewart Strand is leading to destabilisation of the system. Note the skewed distribution of cars along the beach.*

ated with people trampling through the dunes. Dune plants are very sensitive to people pressure and die-back quickly if subjected to too much. Vegetation loss leads to bare ground and eventually sand is blown away by the wind. The worst affected areas are near the beach and near the access (Fig. 12) where the impact of erosion has led to numerous gullies and saucer-shaped blow-outs. However, this is not to say that all bare sand should be eliminated. In fact, the presence of blowouts, avalanche slopes and interdune deflation sheets adds enormously to the habitat variety and appears to be essential in maintaining the

diversity and stability of the dune system (Carter *et al.*, 1990). Since 1982, much of Portstewart dunes has belonged to the National Trust who have made great efforts to introduce effective management, and there has been a marked decline (Fig. 13) in the amount of bare sand at the east end of the strand. The dunes to the east and south (bordering the River Bann) are intensively managed as a golf course. This introduces an artificial but well maintained habitat along the fairways and on the greens. However, the rough remains semi-natural and is often protected against overuse.

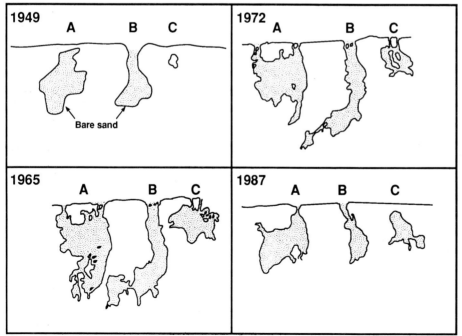

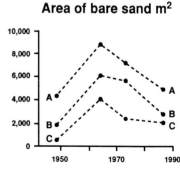

13. *Changing areas of bare sand at the east end of Portstewart Strand since 1949. This area is intensively used for recreation, but since The National Trust assumed ownership in the early 1980s, the amount of bare sand has fallen due to careful management.*

14. *A 1930s photograph of Portstewart Strand showing cars parking on the beach.*

People can drive on the beach, both at Portstewart and Portrush, a practice that dates back to the earliest motor cars (Fig. 14). The impact of this practice is twofold. First, it compacts the beach and reduces sediment transport, and second it damages the beach fauna – which is relatively impoverished. These detrimental effects must be set against the convenience of parking several thousand cars on sunny, summer days and spreading out people along the beach.

The mouth of the River Bann

The mouth of the River Bann is located at a point on the coast where wave energy is relatively low. When first established 5,000 years ago, the River Bann probably flowed out to sea at a rip current location. Once established at the Bann mouth, the channel would be very hard to shift. [There is absolutely no evidence that the River Bann has shifted progressively westwards.]

The tidal flow in the estuary is up to eight times the river flow: the river only dominates the tide during extreme floods. Because of monthly and seasonal discharge fluctuations and the natural variability of the wave field, the Bann mouth was, until the first training walls were built a hundred years ago, a site of constantly shifting sand shoals and channels. There was apparently some pattern to these shifts; material in the channel would accumulate on the east side, pushing the channel towards Castlerock, until it finally switched to the Portstewart side again, and the residual shoal was left to migrate onshore and eventually move sideways and re-enter the estuary channel. In this manner the River Bann acted as a circulatory 'pump', constantly moving sediment through the river mouth. When the training walls were constructed this pumping action was curtailed, for the sake of a deeper, more stable channel (Fig. 15). Unfortunately, the initial engineering works – designed by Sir John Coode, a very eminent Victorian engineer – were not wholly successful as, at times, sand congregated between the piers, causing the larger vessels to 'touch bottom'. Fearful that the continuing sand bar problem would lead to a decline in trade at Coleraine Harbour, more measures were undertaken, including a complete rebuilding of the east and west moles between 1934 and 1941, and later when these were not felt to be satisfactory, even more elaborate plans were drawn up (Hydraulics Research Station, 1957), although never implemented.

In the 1960s and 1970s, the largest size of boats entering the river increased to over 1000 tonnes, and the bar again began to cause problems. On this occasion it was proposed to purchase a dredger, and in 1977 the *Bar Maid* began to remove sediment from the mouth of the river. Since then between 30,000 and 60,000 tonnes of sand have been removed every year and deposited in an EC-designated dump site about 4km to the northwest, from where it seems unlikely that the sand will return to the shore. The amount of

15. *The Bann mouth is confined to a deep channel by two parallel jetties. These jetties have impaired the natural action of the river mouth in recirculating sediment. The sand bar is just visible in front of the boat.*

sand removed between 1977 and 1989 is about 3 to 4 times the volume of the bar, so one must conclude that sediment has migrated into the river mouth to replace that taken out. (Almost all the sand is from the sea side, the river produces very little.) The constant removal of sand may lead to problems for the adjacent shoreline; already there is some evidence of erosion around the moles and on the Portstewart beach nearest the river. Erosion during the 25 February storm in 1990 was concentrated on the dunes around the Bann mouth. Eventually, and the length of time is hard to determine, the river may outflank the training walls and re-establish a wider, more natural mouth.

Portstewart and Portrush

The A2 coast road from Portstewart and Portrush runs parallel to a series of low (<10m) basalt cliffs interspersed with fine examples of boulder and cobble beaches and horizontal shore platforms. This part of the coast is attractive to anglers and the more adventurous holidaymakers, who sun bathe on the rocks and paddle in the pools. However, the cliff-platform system is almost as well-organised in environmental terms as the beach-dune systems described earlier. The platforms are very resistant, so that as the tide rises and falls against them they control the nature of wave activity. At low tide, waves break against the platform and scatter energy. At high tide the platforms act as a step, tripping up the waves and sending

powerful – and dangerous – surges across the rocks. Slowly the waves quarry away the platform, block by block, and the blocks slide and roll landward, accumulating in the boulder beaches. Over the last four to five thousand years the beaches have grown to infill the embayments. During storms, finer material is thrown-up over the beaches to form ramparts against the cliff. Eventually these ramparts grass over and stabilise, creating stretches of active and abandoned cliff. The active cliff shows evidence of occasional block falls or even mass failures, but by and large this coastline is not eroding at any measurable rate.

Portrush – the West Bay

The West, or Mill, Strand at Portrush has been extensively altered by man, beginning with the construction of Portrush Harbour about 1825 and continuing to the present day. The natural beach/dune environment has disappeared and the remaining beach is a poor shadow of its former self.

When the Harbour was built, it altered the inshore wave pattern at the north end of the embayment, and probably led to some localised shoreline erosion. This was exacerbated through damage to the dunes by visitors, especially after the railway opened in 1855 and triggered the expansion of Portrush as a holiday resort. The twentieth century has been marked by a constant battle to protect the shore as the beach has shrunk (Fig. 16).

(A) c.1900

STRAND PROMENADE, PORTRUSH.

16. *The shrinking beach at Portrush may be seen in these views taken over the last 90 years. The former broad strand, has been replaced by a narrower shore, especially in the south (not shown), where the volume of beach material is now extremely limited. All the photos were taken around low spring tide.*

(B) 1963

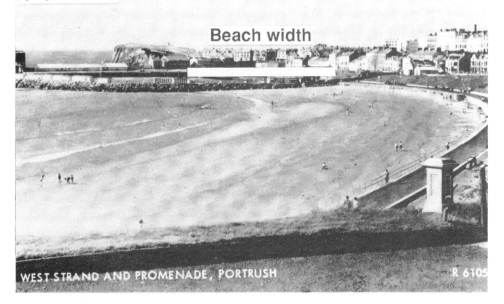

Beach width

WEST STRAND AND PROMENADE, PORTRUSH   R 6105

(C) 1990

Beach width

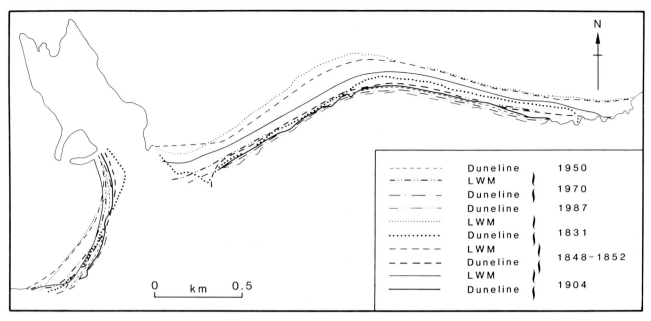

17. *Coastal changes at Portrush may be ascertained by comparing the large-scale OS map since the 1830s.*

Much of the coastal erosion at Portrush (Fig. 17) – on both sides of the town – may be ascribed to human activities. The slow loss of sand, through dredging, commercial extraction and blowing away with the wind, all lead to the gradual retreat of the shoreline. On the West Strand the beach has tried to adjust naturally by becoming graded from relatively coarse material (0.35mm) in the south to fine in the north (0.20mm) but this has not been enough to balance the tendency to erode. Various attempts to protect the shoreline by constructing bulkheads and seawalls, have if anything, made matters worse. The retaining wall built around the Castle Erin hotel (see Fig. 16B) has been instrumental in dividing the beach into two sections, and generating abnormal alongshore currents (Carter, 1975). The southern part of the bay was particularly badly eroded between 1938 and 1952 (Rea, 1981) when the recession rate reached 1.5m/ year.

After many years of public pressure and one false start in the 1940s, a seawall was eventually built around the bay in the early 1960s (sections of wall existed before this), and the natural dunes destroyed. Now storm waves instead of encountering a soft dune, found a hard return wall, which deflected the wave energy seaward. As a result of this change the beach level fell (particularly in the south of the bay), and now where before one could jump safely from the promenade to the beach, one is now in grave danger of breaking both legs. In the worst affected parts, the beach has fallen over a metre and a half (Carter and Bartlett, 1990) and only a thin veneer of beach sand is left. The progressive scouring of the beach has, of course, left the sea wall more liable to damage, and perhaps even collapse. (It must be recorded that this environmental impact of seawalls is well known, and in many places, like Aberystwyth and Porthcawl in Wales, the seawalls have had to be replaced.)

Portrush – the East Strand

The East Strand beach is an unusual convex shape, caused by the wave refraction pattern around the Skerries. If there were enough sand, there would be a tombolo stretching out to the islands.

The East Strand is a highly dissipative beach backed by an extensive area of sand dunes which are occupied by two 18 hole and one 9 hole golf courses. Because of these golf courses, access to the shore is limited to two points at the extreme western and eastern ends, and these areas have suffered a relatively high amount of damage from trampling and more recently motorbikes and all-terrain vehicles (Fig. 18).

The shoreline at Portrush East Strand has receded slowly over the years (Fig. 17), probably due as much to losses from sand extraction than from any natural causes. The development of deep, active blowouts has aided the landward movement of sand.

A number of attempts have been made to control shoreline erosion; at the western end of the beach a low retaining wall *cum* promenade was constructed in the 1960s and the sand hills removed to form a car park. While the wall has performed satisfactorily, it has caused erosion at the eastern end where it abuts the dunes. Here the structure has been undermined to the point of subsidence and waves have scoured the adjacent dune. The badly dissected dune system has been subject to several remedial schemes involving sand fencing, recontouring and vegetation planting and stimulation. In 1974, Enterprise Ulster (a commu-

(A) 1972

100m

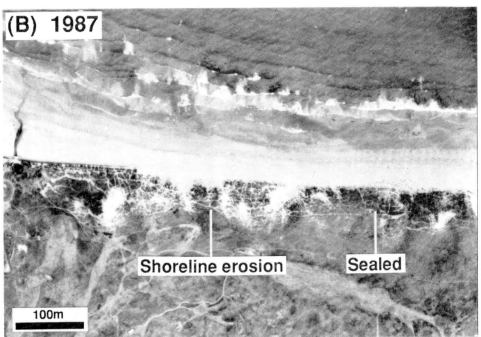

(B) 1987

Shoreline erosion   Sealed

100m

18. The high level of dune degradation at Portrush is due partly to the large number of visitors using only two main access routes. These two photographs illustrate the degree of damage since attempted restoration in 1970. The shoreline has retreated, especially at the end of the seawall.

nity work scheme) undertook to refashion a large area of the most badly eroded dunes, using earthmoving equipment. This experiment, described in (Wilcock and Carter, 1977) has proved successful in stabilising the dune erosion although subsequent management has not been of a particularly high standard. Conventional fencing and planting has been far less effective mainly because there is no adequate supply of fresh sand. Much of the build-up of sand behind fences is just material reworked from adjoining areas.

At the eastern end of the beach – the White Rocks – there has been widespread consternation that shore-line erosion was destroying the famous 5th green on the Royal Portrush Golf Club. To alleviate this possibility the Club undertook, in the early 1980s, a major shore protection scheme using large armour blocks of white chalk, and at the same time regrading and replanting the dune slopes. Later the Golf Club scheme was augmented by Coleraine District Council protection works, using Gabions (wire cages filled with stones) and Netlon, a surface stabilising mesh. These latter works have suffered a certain amount of damage requiring repair, but the Golf Club protection works have stood up well to storms and high tides.

19. The dune cliff faces at Portrush show numerous signs of failure, including small rotational slumps, avalanches and toppling vegetation blocks. The slope form reflects sediment exchange between beach and dune.

The incremental protection of the East Strand is impairing the natural behaviour of the beach. Although occasional storms cut away the dune cliffs, much of the sediment returns to the cliffs over the subsequent few months. The Portrush dunes show magnificent examples of loose granular and low cohesion slope failures (Fig. 19) including small rotational slides and sheet avalanches (Carter, 1980; Carter *et al.*, 1990).

White Rocks to Portballintrae

Some of the hardest rocks in Northern Ireland form the coast between the White Rocks and Portballintrae, a distance of 5km. The white chalk of Cretaceous age forms textbook examples of slope-over-wall cliffs, where the upper vegetated slopes give way to near vertical faces at the shoreline (Fig. 20). The base of the chalk cliff is marked by a distinct wave notch and perhaps fronted by a small shore platform. Cracks, joints or small faults in the rock have been widened to form wave gullies and sea caves. Despite the erosional appearance of chalk cliffs, it is not possible to detect any recent block falls or slope failures. To the east of Dunluce Castle, a fault re-introduces the basalt shoreline, with wider shore platforms, cobble/boulder beaches and storm ramps. This shoreline is more prone to cliff falls. One celebrated example took place

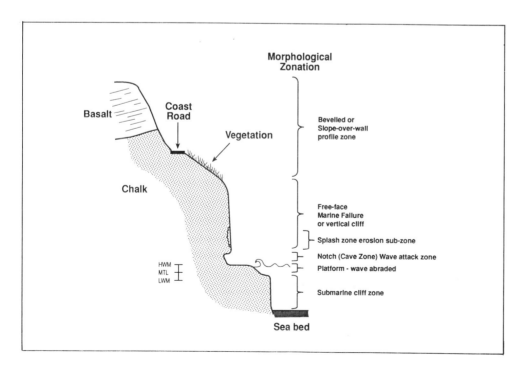

20. The chalk cliffs near the White Rocks show a 'double' slope profile with a steep wave-cut face beneath a flatter, vegetated one. The base of the cliff is notched with a platform in front.

in the 14th century when the kitchens of Dunluce Castle fell into the sea during a banquet (history does not tell us how the news was greeted by the expectant diners!). More recently several shallow earth slides have occurred on this stretch of shoreline, each time bringing down a few tens of cubic metres of vegetation, top soil and rock.

Portballintrae

The coastal problems at Portballintrae have achieved a certain notoriety. There is no dispute that the once sandy beach has turned to an unsightly mixture of gravel and rubbish (Fig. 21) and that the cliffs are eroding, endangering houses and roads. What is not agreed is the cause of all these changes. Locals suggest the beach 'comes and goes' according to some type of mythical cycle, while others accuse various authorities of failing to act.

It is important to establish the facts. As far as can be ascertained, Portballintrae Harbour was formed around 5,000 years ago when the sea was slightly higher than today. Through a combination of sand influx from the adjacent shoreline and the products of slow erosion within the bay itself, Portballintrae developed a well-adjusted, wide sandy beach, with a landward fringe of gravel. This situation appears to have continued until the late nineteenth century, after which the sand has disappeared, at a rate of over 1,000m^3 (c. 200 lorry loads) a year. By 1970 almost all the sand, 80,000m^3, had gone, leaving a residual gravel beach.

Why should this happen? Unfortunately the answer lies yet again with a human cause. While some sand may have been taken away by horse and cart, it is the

21. The once sandy beach at Portballintrae has disappeared leaving a gravel shoreline. The 1935 photograph shows a wide sandy beach (except in the NW) which by the early 1980s had vanished. Most of the material was swept seaward over a submarine cliff and lost into deepwater. The presence or absence of groynes played very little part in the process.

22. *The small pier near Seaport Lodge, the prime cause of erosion at Portballintrae. The remnants of old groynes – introduced too late – can be seen along the shore.*

23. *The first attempts to stabilise the cliff slope at Portballintrae failed because the natural drainage was disrupted causing the slope to collapse. These photographs show (A) a mudflow and (B) tension cracking and slipping.*

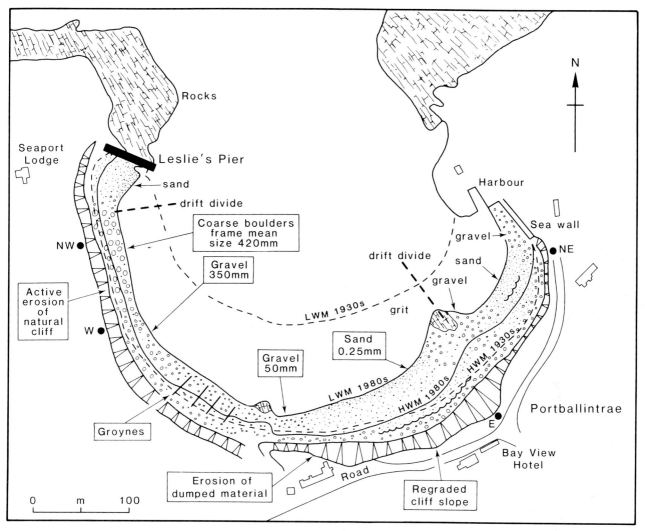

24. *A schematic plan of the bay at Portballintrae showing the sediment grading along the shore.*

innocuous stone pier near Seafort Lodge in the north-west of the bay which is largely to blame (Fig. 22). When this pier was reconstructed and lengthened around 1895 it acted to upset, or perturb the wave pattern within the bay, especially at high tide or during storms. Rather than wave energy spreading out evenly all around the bay, relatively bigger waves began to break in the southwest corner, and perhaps more importantly they began to break at an angle to the shore. This set up a strong southward drift towards the centre of the bay, and sand began to move along the shore. Unfortunately, the sediment that initially accumulated in the centre of the bay later tended to be flushed offshore, passing over a submarine scarp into deep water. It is almost as though someone pulled out a plug, and all the fine sediment drained away.

Measures were taken to try and stop the sand loss. Several sets of groynes were constructed (Fig. 22), the first early this century, the last in the 1970s, but as always it was a case of "too little, too late". As the beach vanished so larger waves were able to erode the backshore, and cliff erosion became a problem. Studies of map and air photographs suggest negligible

erosion rates of the early part of the century (only a few centimetres a year) had increased 20 to 50 fold by 1975, with some parts of the bay losing land at rates of 0.5m/year. While these erosion rates are not particularly high when compared to east Co. Wexford (up to 2m/year) or Holderness in East Yorkshire (up to 3.5m/year), they are bad enough if houses and roads are in danger of falling into the sea. Several attempts have been made to counter the effects of erosion, but none have struck at the cause. Over the last 25 years, about £250,000 has been spent trying to shore-up the shore-line at Portballintrae, with groynes, bulkheads and an expensive, and initially unsuccessful, regrading of the cliff slope (Fig. 23). Experts have come and gone, mostly without solving the problem, with one from London, declaring that the sand loss was merely 'a map error'. Meanwhile the beach has decided to effect its own solution. If you walk along the beach from Seaport Lodge to the Bay View Hotel you will start on sand, then encounter boulders almost too big to scramble over, and then progressively cobbles, gravel, grit and ultimately more sand. In short, the beach has become graded (Fig. 24) (as has the West Strand in

Crescentic Bars

25. *Viewed from the air it is easy to spot the wide crescentic bars that dominate the bay at Runkerry.*

Portrush). This grading enables the beach to balance out the effects of wave action and longshore currents at every point. In time, this grading will slow, and maybe halt, the shoreline erosion more expertly than any engineered solution.

Runkerry (Bushfoot Strand)

To the geomorphologist (a specialist in the study of landforms), Runkerry or Bushfoot strand is the most intriguing of all the northern Irish beaches. Not only do the highest Atlantic waves break here (making it the most dangerous beach in Northern Ireland for swimming but excellent for surfing), but the beach moves from one form to another as the wave energy levels rise and fall. On occasions the beach comprises a narrow strip of cobbles and boulders, etched with beach cusps 20 to 25m in wavelength. These cusps – horseshoe-shaped crescents on the beach – show that wave energy is being reflected and transformed into secondary or resonant edge waves (which move parallel to the beach and decay seaward). These edge waves (which are hard to see) interact with the incoming breakers and cause the surf to run-up the beach in a sinuous, or wave-like pattern. This pattern quickly rearranges the beach material into cusps, which once formed tend to control shore processes until a storm destroys them. At other times, Runkerry will be a flat and wide sandy beach, upon which the waves spill much further offshore. These are dissipative conditions, which set-up inshore water levels and create rip current cells (more danger), similar to those described

at Portstewart (see page 16). Viewed from the air (Fig. 25), the rip current cells are picked-out by crescentric bars, ranging in length from 100 to 250m (Shaw, 1985). The beach 'behaves' by moving periodically from reflective to dissipative states and back again. Lots of beaches move a little, but few as much as Runkerry. The agent of change is dominated by coastal storms, which tend to impose reflective conditions as the finer, sandier sediment is moved offshore. In the 'interstorm' or 'fairweather' periods the dissipative beach reasserts itself.

Runkerry is not a perfect reflective-dissipative system, because the mouth of the River Bush also pumps sediment around, explaining why the south end of the beach is 'sand-rich' while the north end is 'sand-poor'. A lot of sand is also stored in the extensive dune system which covers an area over 200ha. This dune system has suffered quite badly from erosion, caused by walkers, motor-cyclists, and further inland, by grazing and trampling animals.

Giant's Causeway cliffs

With over a quarter of a million visitors a year, the Giant's Causeway is probably the most visited cliff site in the British Isles other than Lands End in Cornwall. Over the years, access to the cliffs has improved, so that today the entire stretch from the Causeway Hotel to Dunseverick Castle (about 6.5km) can be reached on foot.

The Causeway Cliffs (Fig. 26) are a series of embayed 'amphitheatres' cut into the Lower and Middle

26. *The Causeway cliffs are among Europe's most spectacular coastlines.*

27. *About 20,000 years ago the Causeway probably looked like this, hemmed in by an ice pack.*

Giants Eye Glass, Giants Causeway

28. *The collapse of the Giant's Eye Glass in 1949 is one major change that has occurred. These comparative photos show few changes apart from the destruction of the sea arch.*

1986

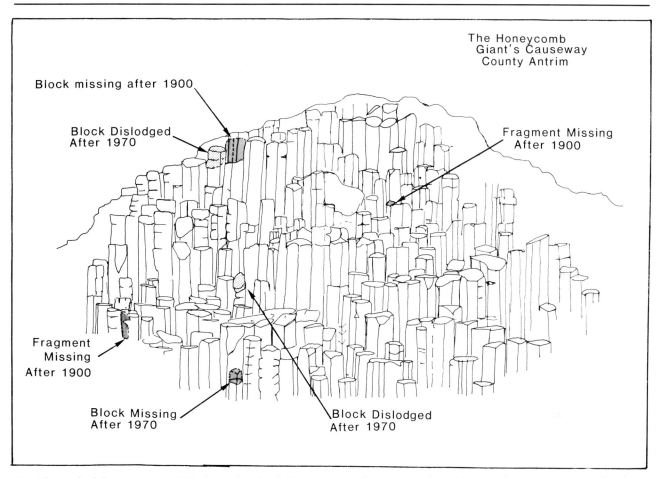

The Honeycomb
Giant's Causeway
County Antrim

Block missing after 1900

Block Dislodged
After 1970

Fragment Missing
After 1900

Fragment
Missing
After 1900

Block Missing
After 1970

Block Dislodged
After 1970

29.   *The gradual disappearance of blocks on the Giant's Causeway may be examined by looking at old and new photographs of the same scene. This example is from The Honeycomb.*

Basalts. These volcanic rocks erupted between 45 and 60 Ma ago into a broad SE-NW valley incised in the underlying chalk. The cooling of the thicker flows, probably in a relatively wet environment, led to the formation of polygonal columnar structures, some of which have been exposed by wave action to form the Giant's Causeway itself.

Much of the coastal scenery dates from the end of the last glaciation (around 25,000 to 17,000 years ago) when, at various times, the ice would have covered and then surrounded the cliffs (Eyles and McCabe, 1989). One can imagine that towards the end of the last glaciation the snow covered cliffs lay along a North Channel filled with pack ice (Fig. 27). Ice sculptured forms were further modified by later periglacial processes, especially the repeated freezing and thawing of the cliff surface which led to the prising-off of rock fragments accumulating along the cliff foot as block falls and screes. To some extent these sub-aerial processes continue today; heavy rainfall and severe frosts are both likely to dislodge blocks from the cliffs, some as big as cars. These may be seen lying on the foreshore.

Although there is plenty of evidence of marine erosion, changes occur only at irregular intervals, and it is impossible to specify an erosion rate for these cliffs. Comparison of photographs, particularly those taken by Robert Welch of Belfast, or for John Lawrence of Dublin in the late 19th or early 20th centuries with modern views reveal both large and small changes at some, but certainly not all, locations. Perhaps the most impressive change has been the collapse of the Giant's Eye Glass – a sea arch – during a storm in 1949 (Fig. 28). At the smaller scale we can trace the disappearance of individual rocks, particularly in much-photographed scenes of the Giant's Causeway. Figure 29 shows the blocks that have gone missing from The Honeycomb. (What of course we don't know is how the blocks were removed. In some cases it is likely children or adults are implicated, but the chaotic accumulations of columnar block beaches suggest the sea has played a part.)

East of the Causeway, especially around Dunseverick Harbour and between White Park Bay and Ballintoy, is some of the best raised beach topography in Ireland. All along this coast a former sea level cut a distinct bench in the chalk and basalt cliffs. Although the age of the raised beach is not known,

30. *Near Dunseverick there is abundant evidence of raised beach forms about 5,000 years old. The old cliffline is now obscured by rock falls.*

it is believed to be associated with the peak sea level around 5,000–6,000 years ago that formed Magilligan and the Portstewart/ Castlerock dunes. As the sea level fell away so it abandoned a series of caves, stacks, arches and platforms (Fig. 30). In places, as the sea level dropped, the shoreline was masked by cliff failures and slope deposits, so that many caves are now hidden from view. There appears to be very little erosion on this stretch of coast, certainly when compared to the Portrush/ Portstewart section which is geologically similar, but more exposed to Atlantic waves.

White Park Bay

White Park Bay is a classic embayment beach, bounded on all sides by geological faults. There are many features of interest here from the "singing sand" which squeaks as you walk over it (due to the extreme roundness of the grains) to the Neolithic kitchen middens found among the dunes. The structure of the bay is clearest on a vertical air photograph (Fig. 31). The meandering shoreline is mirrored in the double crescentric bars which may be seen in the shallow water offshore. These bars, of two distinct wavelengths (170m and 300m), are formed by highly resonant, standing waves (not unlike those formed in the bath tub when you get in or out suddenly), with wave periods of 40 to 50 seconds (Carter and Kitcher, 1979). By and large the bars remain stationary, although during occasional storms they disappear and reform at slightly different wavelengths. Between the bars there are rip currents, again making the beach dangerous for swimming. When the bars change position so the beach changes too. Sand is redistributed along the shore, and at times may lead to localised erosion. However, over a reasonable time frame White Park Bay is a relatively stable beach, with no serious erosion problems. Yet it is threatened by those who take sand, large amounts of which are removed from the beach, and sometimes from the face of the dunes. As far as we know most of the sand is taken for agricultural purposes, but some may find its way into the building trade. We will say more about the sand removal problems when we reach Cushendun and Cushendall (page 000).

The dunes at White Park Bay are formed on a curiously irregular slope, which reaches up to a steep

500m

31. *A vertical air photograph of White Park Bay shows the very confused backslope dune area as well as the small and large crescentic bars.*

inland cliff. In truth, the dunes are little more than a veneer over-lying a major landslip zone. The landslips are moving on a lubricated bed of Liassic clay (which sometimes may be found cropping out on the foreshore to the east of the bay – it is a good rock for fossils). The irregular dune/landslip topography forms a unique environment, a mosaic of wet and dry soils, in which plants of bog and dune may be found side by side. The entire area has been managed by the National Trust since 1933, and the Trust have steadfastly resisted all attempts to improve the access, so that today White Park Bay remains one of our most natural coastline sites, protected from the worst excesses of the tourist trade.

Ballintoy Harbour and Boheeshane Bay

The coast around Ballintoy has been extensively remodelled by man, especially where the Chalk has been quarried, as for example at Larrybane. The coast coincides with a major geological fault – the Port Braddan fault – which runs east-west and brings the black basalt into contact with the white chalk. Many of the caves and crevasses are eroded along small cross

faults and joints, leaving an intricate pattern of small-scale coastal scenery. The rocky outcrops are a source of fragments which have abraded into rounded pebbles and infilled the small bays. These pebbles are coveted for dashing of houses and decorating walls and pathways, and a small industry has grown up, supplying the local building trade. However, the supply of pebbles is very limited and at the current rate of exploitation the pebbles will soon be gone. Some time ago a wall was built to the north of the bay to protect the small harbour. One consequence of this is that instead of the harbour being flushed regularly by waves, it acts as a sediment sink, and boat owners complain of siltation. It is not entirely certain from where this sand comes, but the likelihood is that there is a mobile sand source just to the lee of the rocks guarding the harbour.

Some years ago the University of Ulster installed and maintained a tide gauge at Port Ballintoy. The chart records of tidal rise and fall showed a curious double high water (not unlike the celebrated example in the Solent near Southampton). It is likely this second high water which moves in time and amplitude relative to the primary high water is due to the tidal circulation around Rathlin Island. Even more

29

32. *The tidal 'sundial' (left) on the Church of Ireland at Ballintoy is an enigma, there is no reasonable explanation as to why it should work, as tides are more clearly associated with the moon. The dial is marked by a series of parallel lines in a logarithmic series numbered 1 to 8 and labelled* HIGH WATER HOUR.

curious is the tidal "sundial" on the southwest gable of the church at Ballintoy (Fig. 32). Only about 30% of tidal motion is associated with the sun, the remaining 70% fluctuating in phase with the moon (highest high tides come just after full moons, or at the time of new moons). Perhaps the Ballintoy "sundial" is a "moon-dial", because it is a poor predictor of tides based on the sun. Or perhaps it was an experiment that failed. Whatever the reasons the tide dial is a unique artefact.

Between Ballintoy Harbour and Larrybane is the almost inaccessible Boheeshane Bay. This kilometre-wide bay contains a magnificent set of large cliff falls (Fig. 33). The near-horizontal chalk beds have been undercut by the sea and large blocks – up to 5,000m³ – have toppled seaward. The date of these cliff failures is not known, certainly none are of recent origin.

To the east of Larrybane the coastal cliffs show little evidence of recent change. The limited degree of erosion is evidenced by the lack of debris at the cliff base or in the small beaches, for example at Kenbane Castle.

Rathlin Island

Rathlin Island is separated from the mainland by The Moyle or Rathlin Sound, a strait with a reputation for fierce tides and freak waves. It is a dangerous crossing which has claimed many lives. The strong currents and high waves are caused by tidal streams and Atlantic swell being confined and deflected by the island, turning the strait into a chaotic stretch of water. Waves approaching from the west pass both to the north and south of Rathlin. Those on the north side swing right around the eastern-most point – Rue Point – and then move *west*, crossing and colliding with the easterly swell moving along the south coast. Where two waves cross, they grow rapidly in height, and powerful currents may flow for a few moments. These waves are a danger, particularly to those who do not anticipate them.

The coast of Rathlin is predominantly rocky, with only the small re-entrant at Church Bay sporting beaches of any kind. Some of the material from this beach is collected for pebble-dashing houses, and quantities are shipped to Ballycastle.

The rock cliffs, with their limited access, support extensive populations of seabirds, who feed all along the north coast of Ireland. The cliffs show signs of occasional rock falls but the retreat rates of the cliffs are too low to be measured. The offshore area is particularly rich in plants and animals (Erwin *et al*, 1986 and 1990), and may eventually become a marine nature reserve.

Ballycastle

At Ballycastle the coast changes. The high-energy Atlantic beaches formed of well-sorted sediments of shelf origin give way to medium-energy shorelines composed of coarser, more poorly sorted alluvial (river borne) materials. The tidal range at Ballycastle (1.2m on springs) is among the lowest in Ireland. To

the north near Muckaranish on the Mull of Kintyre the tide range is zero. This is the site of an amphidromic point, around which tides revolve. The further one goes away from an amphidromic point the higher the tidal range becomes. Thus, both west and south from Fair Head the tide range increases to 3.1 metres at Malin and over 4.0 metres in Dundrum Bay.

During the last glaciation a vast amount of sediment was deposited inland of Ballycastle (Fig. 34). The Carey Valley in particular is choked with glacial sands and gravels arranged in the form of deltas. The traditional explanation of these deltas was that a large, but slow-draining lake formed towards the end of the ice age [18,000 years ago], supplied by water and sand from an ice sheet filling Glendun to the south. Recently, and perhaps controversially, it has been suggested (McCabe and Eyles, 1988), that the deltas are *submarine* forms, meaning that the sea level was very much higher than previously suspected. While this is a point of debate, what is clear is that very large quantities of deltaic sands and gravels were transported downstream during floods, perhaps even in sudden bursts of icy water lasting only a few hours, called 'jokulaups' in Iceland where they often occur in early summer as the winter snows melt and the rivers begin to unblock.

The deposits of these events may be found throughout the lower valley, often in the form of alluvial or river terraces. Some of this alluvial material reached the shoreline, and has been reworked, resorted and incorporated by wave and wind action into the pres-

33. *Boheeshane Bay includes some of the best rockfall features in Ireland In this photograph a large block is toppling slowly into the sea.*

34. *The sediment that forms Ballycastle Beach almost certainly derives from the Carey Valley and Glenshesk which are choked with glacial debris, and include a major suite of abandoned deltas.*

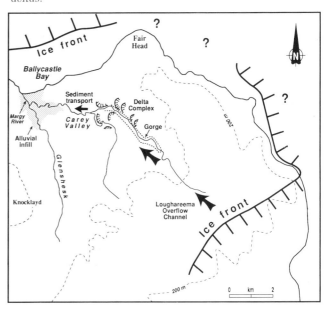

35. *Ballycastle Beach comprises a microtidal gravel beach fronted by a flat, sandy, subtidal zone.*

ent Ballycastle Strand (Fig. 35). The Strand comprises two elements. Firstly there is a narrow, coarse-grained beach backed by a low cliff incised into a river terrace, but with a cap of aeolian dunes. This beach often displays cusps 20 to 40 metres across filling the entire 1.5km length of the bay. These cusps are regularly re-cut as wave conditions change. Secondly, there is a shallow sub-tidal slope with crescentic bars, akin to those found at Runkerry and White Park Bay. This double form indicates the transitional nature of Bally-castle, between the Atlantic swell wave environment and the Irish Sea sea waves.

The incoming waves tend to generate a net westerly-moving longshore current so that the tendency is for material to accumulate near the mouth of the Margy River. Before large-scale channelisation of the inland rivers, it seems likely that the westerly, wave-induced

drift was balanced by the pumping action of the river mouth, acting to recirculate material throughout the entire embayment. More recently, the power of this pumping action has declined, allowing a gradual reorganisation of the coastal sediments, with a loss at the eastern end (towards Pans Rock) being offset by a gain near the river mouth.

This slow change must be borne in mind when examining the 'erosion-problem' at Ballycastle, which has caused a lot of agitation amongst local people. A comparison of maps and photographs reveals few long term changes, with a maximum erosion rate of only about 0.15m/year since 1935 and virtually no change prior to this. Old drawings and photographs (Fig. 36) show that many of the prominent shore features are little changed since 1800. The erosion problem must be considered in its human context. A

36. *An old painting c.1828 by Andrew Nichol (1804–1886) of the eastern end of Ballycastle Beach. Many of the shore features shown on this scene can be found in the same places today.*

lot of the shoreline is 'made-ground' created in the 18th century when a road was built between the salt pans, coalfield, and the Ballycastle Glassworks (1754 onwards), and it is largely this material that is eroding during occasional storms. In addition, most damage has taken place near the ends of sea walls or where people have destroyed the narrow duneline. A more indirect cause of erosion may arise from the former practice of taking sand from the old harbour (just west of the Margy) to cover the town rubbish dump, or the small-scale but ongoing problem of sand and pebble removal from the beach.

All these factors complicate resolution of the relatively- limited erosion problem, although some low cost shore protection and landscaping has recently been completed by Ballycastle Golf Club.

Ballycastle to Cushendun

To the east of Ballycastle the shoreline is formed in a variety of igneous and sedimentary rocks of different ages, durabilities and weathering potential. In Colliery Bay, the Carboniferous sandstones are particularly prone to salt- weathering (McGreevey, 1985) and the intertidal zone displays numerous small-scale erosion forms like rock pedestals, joint cracks, etch pits, potholes and pans (Fig. 37). A particularly good high to low water zonation of weathering is found on

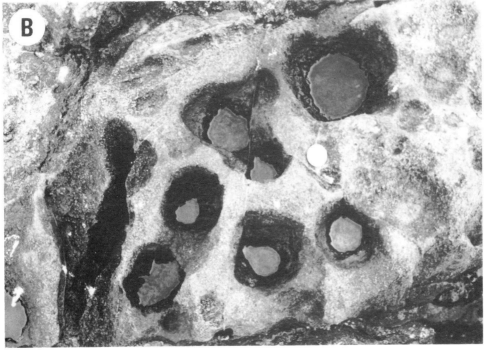

37. *Erosion forms on the shoreline near Pans Rocks at Ballycastle are associated with salt weathering. (A) shows etched joints, while (B) illustrates micropits a few centimetres across.*

33

38. *The rock talus cliffs of Fair Head probably date back to the late-glacial period, 19,000–20,000 years ago.*

Pans Rock. Around Fair Head, the horizontal dolerite sill results in a 120m high cliff, fronted by an extensive apron of rock talus (Fig. 38), with many individual blocks several metres in diameter. It seems likely that this cliff was formed during the dissolution of the last ice sheet, when very active freezing and thawing would have provided the mechanism for dislodging such large blocks.

At Fair Head, the coast changes direction from east-west to north south. In many ways, Fair Head marks the boundary between the Atlantic and the Irish Sea. Murlough Bay, one of the most beautiful bays in Co. Antrim, differs from almost all the others in that it has no apparent source of loose (clastic) sediment, other than that derived directly from erosion of the shore. There is no major stream entering the coast here, and the offshore zone is steep enough to preclude the onshore movement of loose debris. In their sub-aqueous investigations, Erwin *et al.* (1986) found a current-scoured seabed, with a holdfast community (sea-weeds etc.), suggesting very little sediment movement is now taking place.

Taken together, these environmental factors explain why the shoreline of Murlough Bay is composed of ill-sorted gravels, cobbles and boulders derived mostly from occasional down slope movements and dislodgement by wave action.

The sediment-starved nature of the coast continues, via Torr Head, to Cushendun. Long stretches of hard rock cliffs and overhanging slopes are broken only irregularly by small, poorly sorted accumulations of coarse beach material, as for example at Port-aleen and Loughan. There are no records of recent coastal changes along any of this coast, although air photographs reveal a small number of small earth slides and rock falls.

Cushendun

Cushendun lies at the mouth of Glendun. A relatively small (1km) beach is interrupted at the south end by the exit of the Glendun River, and to the north by the much smaller Milltown Burn. The offshore zone at Cushendun comprises a hard calcareous substratum mixed with patches of very coarse shell sand although there are some indications that low-relief crescentic bars exist at times. This suggests there is little fresh sediment available from the seaward side to augment the meagre beach. In fact, the beach material, despite having been reworked by the waves, is more characteristic of river and glacial sands found throughout the Glendun valley up to and including the deposits on the east flank of Slieveanorra. Further inspection of coastal land, suggests the present beach is cut into an abandoned river terrace (locally termed The Warren), which has been 'decorated' with a thin cover of wind-blown sand. So, in essence, the beach may be considered a closed morphological unit, within which sand is circulated through the combined actions of the waves and river currents (Fig. 39). Left to itself, a grain of sand would be taken seaward by the expanding and decelerating river flow and then gradually returned shorewards to the beach, some distance along the shore. In time, waves and longshore currents would drift the grain southwards, back into the river mouth and the cycle would restart.

Unfortunately, the beach has not been left to behave naturally. An erosion 'problem' was diagnosed some years ago and measures taken to effect a solution. Perhaps more importantly, the river mouth has been altered, starting as far back as the mid-eighteenth century when harbour 'improvements' were put in train. The results of dredging and channelising are

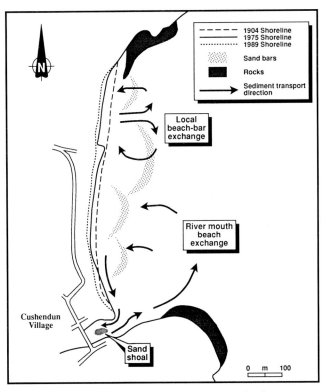

39. *A sketch showing the probable movement of sediment in Cushendun Bay, plus an indication of shoreline change.*

based on tradition rather than any written statute). Historically, the taking of sand was a relatively time consuming business, so that perhaps each farmer took only one or two loads a year, just to lighten the heavy clay soils. While not an environmentally benign action, such a scale of operations could be accommodated. But in the last 30 years many of the previously existing ground rules have changed. The introduction of front-loading tractors and JCBs make it much easier and quicker to take sand (see Fig. 48). Better roads mean that it can be taken further inland, and a general intensification of the farming practices and infrastructures have increased the need for fine aggregates, like sand and gravel, so that beach material is now used to improve trafficability around field gates, as a constituent in livestock-house flooring, for construction of concrete paths and outbuildings, packing for field drains as well as the more traditional land-improvement operations. Significant non-agriculture uses are also found, especially for dressing sports pitches, covering or infilling dumps, providing childrens' play areas and so forth. All this has meant increasing pressure on those beaches traditionally viewed as sources of 'free' sand. But, as is often pointed-out, there is no such thing as 'free', and in this case the cost must be measured against increasing shoreline recession and perhaps the eventual threatening of houses and roads by erosion.

How much sand goes from Cushendun beach is not known, but a conservative estimate would be 300 loads a year, which translates to a figure of 45,000 cubic metres lost since 1960. This amount is almost equal to the quantity of mobile sand on the present day beach. Under such pressure, and with no fresh sand available the beach takes from the low backshore cliffs and the shoreline retreats. Before 1960, the erosion rate in the bay was low, only 0.1 to 0.2m/year, enough to maintain a low cliff, but not to threaten seriously the houses or the road. After 1960, the erosion accelerated, reaching 0.6m/year to the north by 1975, and 0.8m/year in the south since 1980 (Fig. 40). This

that the river mouth has become progressively cut-off from the beach, thus breaking a natural cycle. The recent (1987) construction (and subsequent reconstruction in 1990) of an armour breakwater has simply been the most recent in a long line of attempts to 'fiddle' with the shoreline.

Meanwhile, back at the beach, more difficulties have arisen. Cushendun, along with at least sixteen other sites on the Antrim coast, has always provided local farmers with a convenient source of sand. This constitutes a prescriptive right, enshrined in Common Law (a right handed on from generation to generation,

40. *Coastline recession at Cushendun since 1960 has accelerated sharply. When they were inserted the wooden piles were about 2m from the cliff, they are now over 12m away.*

means that in the last 10 years the shoreline has receded by 6 to 8 metres, or the width of a tarmaced highway. The correlation between the increased sand removal activities and the increased erosion is clear, the dilemma is 'what to do about it?'. The Crown Estate Commissions who own the beach, the National Trust who lease and manage it, and the Department of the Environment are all seeking solutions, which may eventually curb the erosion. One recently mooted possibility is to provide a supply of non-beach sand for local farmers.

Cushendall

The problems at Cushendun may be put into context by examining the neighbouring beach at Cushendall. This beach bears a remarkable similarity both in size and setting to Cushendun.

When old maps are compared, it is apparent that Cushendall had one of the most serious erosion problems on the Antrim coast. Between 1903 and 1963 the beach retreated about 45 metres, equal to a rate of 0.65 m/year (Fig. 41). This alarming rate of retreat can be discerned from photographs taken during this period (Fig. 42), as the grass field in front of what is now the golf club house shrinks dramatically. Despite the rapid erosion, the *volume* of material involved (about 33,000 cubic metres) is not great, particularly when compared to the amounts of sand moved around on some of the North Coast beaches. However, the severe erosion problem was controlled by the building of a low sea wall in 1963. This has acted to hold the shoreline itself, although it has also been responsible for changing the character of the beach, which has gone from a relatively wide (c. 35m) sandy beach, capable, as one local puts it, of 'burying a cow', to being a narrow, gravelly one, particularly in the north away from the mouth of the River Dall. The reason why Cushendall beach eroded must be due to the removal of sand over a long period. The recession rate is equivalent to the taking of about 100 loads of sand a year, or one every 3 to 4 days. This is not an excessive amount when viewed in these terms, but the cumulative effect can be demonstrated to spell disaster for small beaches like those at Cushendun and Cushendall.

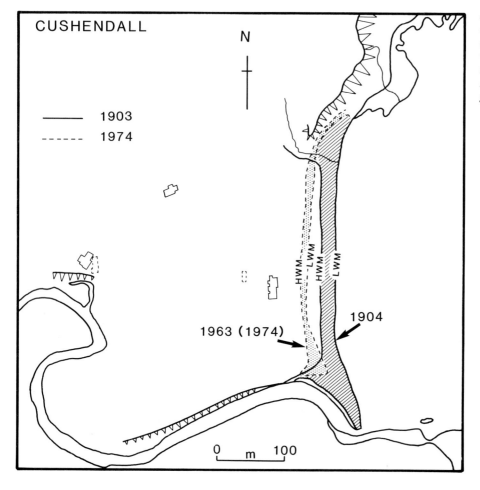

41. *The beach at Cushendall retreated by over 70m before a sea wall was built in 1963. After this the beach became narrower and more gravelly.*

(A) c.1925

c. 100m

(B) c.1960

c. 25m

42. *Photographs taken at various times this century show the retreat of the shoreline before the sea wall was constructed. (B) © E.T.W. Dennis & Sons Ltd., Scarborough.*

Red Bay and Waterfoot

Three kilometres south of Cushendall, the entrance to Glenariff is occupied by Red Bay, with the village of Waterfoot nestling in the north corner. The cliffs along the northern shore contain evidence of raised beach features, including stacks and caves (Prior, 1966), suggesting the sea may have penetrated further inland at one time. The coastal sediments are more reminiscent of those found on the North Coast, which indicates that at this site, the bulk of the sands and gravel may have come from the adjacent shelf, rather than from simple reworking of valley sediments. The shoreline

comprises several distinct elements, including an active river mouth where the Glenariff enters the sea, a series of low dunes, and a predominantly sandy beach. The dunes include clumps of Sea Lyme grass *Leymus arenarius*, an uncommon plant on this coast, as well as fertile stands of Sea Buckthorn *Hippophae rhamnoides* (see page 38) which was probably planted to help protect the foredunes from being damaged by visitors. At the centre of the bay, the natural dunes have been quarried away, leaving a zone of low-lying ground now occupied by a pitch and putt golf course. The whole shoreline shows signs of erosion, although no long term trend is apparent. Low cost sea defenses have been tried at various points, especially near the caravan site and around some of the shorefront properties, with varying degrees of success. There appears to be a slight tendency for material to drift north, towards the mouth of the Glenariff River, which requires periodic dredging to maintain a navigable channel.

Red Bay to Carnlough

From Red Bay to Carnlough the coast is rocky, and the morphology is dominated by the complexities of the underlying geology. The margins of the plateau, composed of basalt overlying chalk, rests on an unstable layer of Liassic clay, which accounts for the large number of slope failures along this stretch of coast. It would be incorrect to dismiss the sea as a factor in the many slope movements, as wave action provides (or provided) the mechanism for removing much of the slumped material. But the fact remains that many of the landslips and earth slumps are controlled by the hydrogeology of the Antrim Plateau. There are three basic categories of scarp instability, differing in magnitude and frequency of occurrence. The largest and most infrequent are the rotational landslips (Fig. 43), best seen around Garron Point but common all along the Plateau Scarp from Benbradagh near Dungiven in County Londonderry to Cave Hill

near Belfast (a distance of about 170km). These very large failures are a tantamount to geological faults, occurring at infrequent intervals. It is most likely that many landslips occurred at the end of the last glacial period, when the land was 'relaxing' as the loading of ice was decreasing, and there was abundant water to act as a lubricant, aiding slippage. Much smaller and more frequent (on a scale of hundreds of years) are landslips. These can be seen in fossil form all along the coast (Fig. 44). Many became stabilised once the coast road was constructed and the sea could no longer attack the toe of the slip. Finally, there are many small, superficial rockfalls, slips and slides often involving only a few blocks or cubic metres of soil and failing at frequent intervals. Often, it is possible to detect where such slips might occur because the slope is corrugated into staircases of small features called 'terracettes'. These indicate a slow, downhill 'creep' of the soil layer, indicating that the slope is very close to the angle of failure.

The unstable slopes contribute sediment both directly to the coast and indirectly via small, steep gradient streams like the Ardclinis Burn, the Carnlough River and the Black Burn. Debris washed down these streams, probably following heavy rainfall or snow melt on the surrounding hills, forms small deltas all along this shore.

Nonetheless the shoreline along this stretch of coast

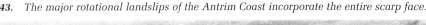

43. *The major rotational landslips of the Antrim Coast incorporate the entire scarp face.*

44. *Minor slope instabilities are clearly visible along much of the coast. These examples are from Minnis North and show an active mud-flow, several inactive and fossil ones as well as terracettes (parallel ridges across the slope).*

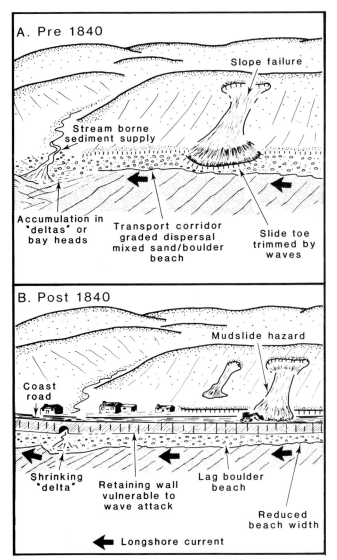

is relatively starved of sediment, which for the most part comprises outcrops of rock platform and boulder clusters. Although the dominant drift is southwards, driven by the dying residuals of the Atlantic swells, it is difficult for material to make substantial progress along the rough, irregular shoreline. As it moves south, an individual clast will constantly be imprisoned (perhaps for decades) before being released to move a little further downcoast before being recaptured. The small deltas both catch and release sediment, but in general they act as magnets for deposition, slowly accumulating debris. Very often the deltas show sediment grading from coarser, angular material at the river mouths to finer, rounder materials on the flanks.

Before the coast road was built in the 1830s we may imagine the slow but persistent delivery of material to be moved by the waves (Fig. 45A). Gradually this material accumulated at river mouths, in small re-entrant bays and even behind large rocks. But the road put a stop to much of this slowly moving transport system, and gradually as the supply dwindled, the small pocket beaches began to disappear (Fig. 45B), either naturally or carted away by farmers. The biggest accumulations at Carnlough and Glenarm still survive, but many smaller beaches have gone altogether.

45. *Cartoons to show the likely environmental impact of the Antrim Coast Road on the sediment budget. In A there is unimpeded longshore transport, in B the beach is starved of material, and slow erosion sets in.*

39

Carnlough and Glenarm

The two beaches at Carnlough and Glenarm lie at the foot of Glencoy and Glenarm respectively. The beaches are a mixture of gravel and sand, which appears to have come from both inland and along the shore. Carnlough embayment forms the downdrift 'sink' of 8km of slowly eroding cliff, and over the last few thousand years sediment has accumulated as a series of prograding ridges, the largest of which are landward of the A2 coast road in the lower part of the Glencoy valley. Mesolithic remains have been discovered on these ridges suggesting they are several thousand years old. Some years ago on

the present foreshore, two peat layers were found, indicating that 9,000 years ago the sea was at a somewhat lower level than today (Prior et al, 1981). Thus the gravel ridges formed between 6,000 and 9,000 years before present, which fits well with evidence from elsewhere (see page 5).

Map evidence suggests that few changes have occurred on this beach, certainly there is no sign of rapid recession, like that observed further north. However, this evidence belies the fact that a former gravel beach that fronted the north end of the bay has vanished (Fig. 46). This old beach provided ample protection to the coast road, but was later reinforced by a low masonry wall, probably to

c.1950

46. *Earlier this century the seawall at Carnlough was fronted by a substantial gravel beach. These photographs show the changes over the last 40 years.*

1989

guard against stones being thrown-up during storms. Also the ridge was gradually becoming thinner and therefore more liable to move as the updrift supply from the landslips failed. The early wall was later replaced around 1960 by the present sea wall (McTaggert and Scott, 1966). Together these seawalls appear to have encouraged the gravel beach to go away. It is easy to see why. During storms the waves would reflect from the solid wall, instead of soaking into the gravel, and the new seaward-moving currents so created would mobilise the gravel, which would slide, skip and roll away across the flat intertidal apron. Most likely, the gravel has simply moved downdrift and augmented the present gravel

beach in the south of the bay, but whatever its fate it has left the seawall very badly exposed (Fig. 47) and looking the worse for wear, with many examples of split and lifted concrete blocks.

The little beach at Glenarm is a mixture of river and shore material swept into a small bay. There is a good example of a delta just north of the beach, formed of more angular river borne material. Glenarm beach is the location for gravel winning activities (Fig. 48), very often several tractors may be on the shore at one time. Under such intense pressure it seems unlikely the gravel resource will survive for long.

47. *The seawall at Carnlough is in a very poor state of repair.*

48. *Sediment removal from the beach at Glenarm.*

Glenarm to Larne

The 15km of coast south of Glenarm is very similar to that from Red Bay to Carnlough. The Antrim Coast Road skirts the shore, often running along the so-called '25 foot' raised beach. The cliffs display many examples of land instabilities, including the scientifically famous mudslides at Minnis North (see Fig. 44) which were extensively studied by the Queen's University of Belfast in the 1960s and 1970s (Prior *et al*, 1968; Hutchinson *et al*, 1974). At times, these mudslides move quickly and unpredictably and are considered potentially dangerous. The slides are triggered by varying groundwater pressures, and result in considerable volumes of liquid mud descending onto, and often blocking, the main A2 road. Before the road was built this material would have supplied the littoral drift although most of the clay would have floated away.

For much of the distance, the coast road runs along a raised beach. The now-abandoned cliff, mostly cut in boulder clay, is often prominent on the landward side of the road, as for example, north of Ballygalley or around Drain's Bay. The raised beach is a mixture of erosional and depositional landforms and the notch or abrupt change of slope at the base of cliff is not always a true reflection of the former height of the sea. Much of the coast, where not protected by the sea wall, shows signs of sporadic erosion, usually in the form of a low wave-cut cliff or terrace at the back of the beach. What transportable sediment there is moves to the south, accumulating behind small obstructions (slipways, pipes, boulders) and in the small re-entrant bays, such as at Closeburn or Ballygalley. Sediment deficit and the onset of erosion probably led to the construction of a seawall at Ballygalley (Fig. 49) where the beach is now very low.

It seems unlikely that much sediment passes around Ballygalley Head, yet the next segment of coast, from Carnfunnock to Larne terminates in a major deposit of beach gravel at the mouth of Larne Harbour (Fig. 50). Clearly this sediment, several hundred thousand cubic metres, must have been derived at some time from the erosion of the adjacent shoreline. Beach gravels are notoriously mobile. They tend to remain in the wave zone and where there is a persistent longshore current, they move rapidly downdrift. Such gravels accumulate where and when wave energy falls. In the period 5,000 to 8,000 years ago, as sea level rose, conditions around Larne would have been ideal. Gravel-rich beaches fed by rapid shoreline erosion and influenced by southerly-moving waves would have pumped sediment into the relatively calm waters of Larne Lough, forming a complex spit system. As the sea level fell, the sediment supply would have fallen, and at this time the spit began to rework itself into a series of 'cells' (Fig. 51). The beach gravels

49. *The coast at Ballygalley shows a low sea wall and depleted beach levels.*

50. *The Curran photographed in the late 19th Century. Two distinct cells are visible with major gravel recurves.*

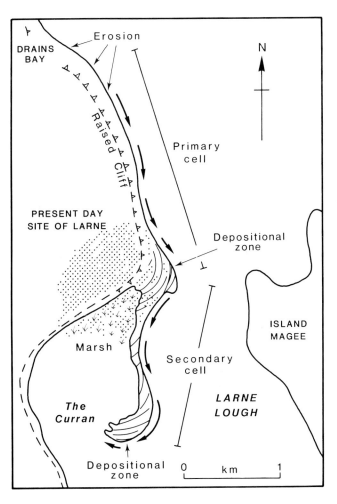

51. *A diagrammatic view of the gravel ridge development at Larne. Material from the north has been deposited as it enters the Lough.*

contained a high proportion of flint (from the chalk) and this was worked by early man into distinctive tools (arrow leads, axes etc.) so that the culture is termed "Larnian" (Mitchell, 1971).

Although it is still possible to find 'worked' flints at Curran Point, very little of the natural environment remains. The old spits (as in Fig. 51) have largely disappeared under port developments, and much of the remaining land is derelict.

FUTURE MANAGEMENT

___

The northeast coast of Ireland is one of great value. It is an important resource and should be carefully managed for future generations to enjoy. On a national scale, the rate of coastal changes is not great (Carter and Bartlett, 1990), with even the average erosion falling well below that found in eastern Ireland (south of Dublin) and along much of the east coast of England. Table 5 summarises the erosion rates for the 'soft' coasts (beaches and dunes), but it is impossible to give an equivalent figure for the 'hard' coasts (cliffs), beyond noting that they are subject to slow, irreversible change.

Coast erosion is a complex problem. In northeast Ireland erosion is caused by both natural and man-related processes, in different proportions at each site. The traditional management of such problems has been to build sea defences, usually seawalls, bulkheads or armour blocks. Groynes are often proposed, but except in local areas, they are rarely effective. Engineers seek *reliable* solutions; after each damaging storm they tend to suggest more effective (and often more expensive!) solutions. Yet it is well-known that many shore defenses create their own erosion problems – for example the seawalls at Portrush and Carnlough – and eventually need to be replaced with stronger structures as the natural protection of the beaches and dunes has been lost. This may be described as a 'policy trap', as the taxpayer finds him- or herself committed to ever greater financing to solve a problem created by a problem. In contrast, the environmental scientist seeks *resilient* solutions. These aim to find the most beneficial mix of plans and techniques to offset (or mitigate) the problem. For coastal erosion, an environmental scientist would recommend low-cost shore protection, land zoning and property adjustment (including the paying of compensation) to counter the threat of coastal change. Not only is this often far more environmentally friendly, it is also cheaper and therefore more likely to be cost-effective. In Northern Ireland, the Department of the Environment is taking considerable interest in these alternative strategies for coastal protection, as they tend to retain and even enhance the beauty of the coast. The spectre of further erosion arising from climatic change and future sea-level rise is also with us. While it is unlikely that Northern Ireland will be affected in the near future (certainly not before 2030 AD), it would be prudent to plan for such major impacts perhaps by restricting building in vulnerable sites.

It is wrong to equate coastal problems in northeast Ireland solely with shoreline erosion, although this process is the manifestation of a wide range of impacts. The coastal system suffers from a variety of inter-related stresses including over-provision of access, lowering of biological productivity, disruption of food chains, disposal of waste and so on. Perhaps less obvious is that what we do inland may affect the coast. The modification of our rivers, the application of fertilisers and changes in our patterns of social and cultural activities may all have ramifications for our coastline. Some of these effects are easy to trace, while others are far removed in space and in time, and are rarely obvious. It is often difficult to perceive coastal change. This may happen in two ways. First, many people are convinced that the beaches they used to visit a generation or so ago have altered radically. We are constantly regaled with tales of past shorelines hundreds of yards further seaward than today or of rocks that were never exposed, which now protrude several metres above the beach. Although there is often some truth in these statements, the memory is being overexaggerated, and careful assessment usually reveals changes of a much lower magnitude. Second, some people cannot visualise links between events. Damage in storms is not equated with benefits during calmer weather. People who regularly draw sand from the beaches often see no connection between their actions and accelerating erosion. It is important that future generations be informed over coastal matters.

The challenge of the next few years will be to devise a sensible management plan to retain the value of the coast of northeast Ireland. This may evolve through a combination of education and encouragement, especially through agencies like The National Trust, the District Councils and the Northern Ireland Department of the Environment.

Table 5. Coast erosion rates

Site	Dates	Average Rate of shoreline change, m/year (+ accretion, - erosion
Magilligan		
Lough Foyle	1833–1966[1]	-0.75
	1949–1980[2,3]	-0.84
Mount Sandy	1833–1966[1]	-1.23
	1949–1985[2,3]	-2.56
Benone	1833–1966[1]	+0.08
	1850–1904[1]	+0.10
Castlerock[4]	1904–1970[1]	+0.11
Portstewart[4]	1850–1904[1]	-0.06
	1904–1970[1]	+0.06
	1949–1982[2]	+0.05
Portrush		
Westy Bay[5]	1850–1950[1]	+0.15
East Strand	1850–1904[1]	-0.14
	1904–1966[1]	-0.08
	1950–1987[2]	-0.12
Portballintrae	1833–1904[1]	<-0.03
	1904–1966[1]	-0.15
	1949–1975[2]	-0.25
Runkerry	1904–1970	-0.04
(Bushfoot)		
White Park Bay	1904–1971[1]	-0.11
Ballycastle	1904–1933[1]	-0.17
	1933–1987[1,2]	-0.17
Cushendun	1004–1963[1]	-0.21
South	1963–1975[2]	-0.11
South	1975–1987[3]	-1.08
North	1963–1975[2]	-1.01
Cushendall[6]	1903–1963[1]	-0.79
Waterfoot	1912–1987[1]	-0.26
Carnlough	1903–1950[1]	-0.36

Sources:
1. Ordnance Survey maps
2. Air photographs
3. Ground surveys

Jetties built:
4. 1883–1888 and 1934–1941

Sea walls built:
5. 1949–1963
6. 1963
7. c. 1950–1951

BIBLIOGRAPHY

The following books are recommended as general reading on coastal processes and management. They all contain more specific information and indications of further reading.

Boaden, P.J.S. and Seed, R. 1986, *An Introduction to Coastal Ecology*, Blackie, Glasgow.

Brown, A.C. and McLachlan, A. 1990, *Ecology of Sandy Shores*, Elsevier, Amsterdam.

Carter, R.W.G. 1988, *Coastal Environments*, Academic Press, London.

Clark, R.B. 1989, *Coastal Pollution* (2nd Ed.), Clarendon Press, Oxford.

Furness, P. and Monaghan, P. 1987, *Ecology of Seabirds*, Blackie, Glasgow.

Hansom, J.D. 1989, *Coasts*, Cambridge University Press, Cambridge.

McCluskey, D. 1989, *The Estuarine Environment* (2nd Ed.) Blackie, Glasgow.

Pethick, J.S. 1984, *An Introduction to Coastal Geomorphology*, Arnold, London.

REFERENCES

Bowen, D.Q. (1978) *Quaternary Geology* Pergamon Press.

Carter, R.W.G. (1975) The effects of human pressures on the coastlines of counties Londonderry and Antrim. *Irish Geography*, 8, 70–85.

Carter, R.W.G. (1980) Human activities and coastal processes: the example of recreation in Northern Ireland. *Zeitschrift für Geomorphologie, Supplementeband*, 34, 155–164.

Carter, R.W.G. (1982a) Coastal caravan sites in Northern Ireland 1960–1980 *Irish Geography*, 15, 107–111.

Carter, R.W.G. (1982b) Sea-level changes in Northern Ireland. *Proceedings Geologists' Association, London*, 93, 7–23.

Carter, R.W.G. (1982c) Recent variations in sea level on the east and north coasts of Ireland. *Proceedings of the Royal Irish Academy*, 82B, 177–187.

Carter, R.W.G. (1986) The morphodynamics of beach ridge formation at Magilligan, Northern Ireland. *Marine Geology*, 73, 191–214.

Carter, R.W.G. (1987) Man's response to change in the coastal zone of Ireland. *Resource Management and Optimization*, 5, 127–164.

Carter, R.W.G. and Bartlett, D.J. (1988) *Coastal Erosion and Management in the Glens of Antrim and Causeway Coast Areas of Outstanding Natural Beauty*, Department of the Environment, Northern Ireland, 152pp.

Carter, R.W.G. and Bartlett, D.J. (1990) Coast erosion in north east Ireland: Part I – Beaches, dunes and river mouths. *Irish Geography*, 23, 1–16.

Carter, R.W.G. and Kitcher, K.J. (1979) The geomorphology of offshore sand bars on the north coast of Ireland. *Proceedings of the Royal Irish Academy*, 79B, 43–61.

Carter, R.W.G. and Wilson, P. (1990) Geomorphological, ecological and pedological development of coastal foredunes at Magilligan Point, Northern Ireland. In, Nordstrom, K., Psuty, N. and Carter, R.W.G. (eds.) *Coastal Dunes*, John Wiley, Chichester, 129–157.

Carter, R.W.G., Devoy, R.J.N. and Shaw, J. (1989) Late Holocene sea-level changes in Ireland. *Journal of Quaternary Science*, 4, 7–23.

Carter, R.W.G., Hesp, P.A. and Nordstrom, K.F. (1990) Erosional landforms in coastal dunes. In, Nordstrom, K., Psuty, N. and Carter, R.W.G. (eds.) *Coastal Dunes*, John Wiley, Chichester, 217–250.

Carter, R.W.G., Lowry, P. and Stone, G.W. (1982) Ebb shoal control of shoreline erosion via wave refraction, Magilligan Point, Northern Ireland. *Marine Geology* 48, M17–M25.

Devoy, R.J.N. (1985) The problems of a late-Quaternary land bridge between Britain and Ireland. *Quaternary Science Reviews* 4, 43–58.

Erwin, D.G., Picton, B.E., Connor, D.W., Howson, C.M., Gilleece, P. and Bogues, M.J. (1986) *The Northern Ireland Sublittoral Survey*, Ulster Museum, Belfast 127pp. + appendices.

Erwin, D.G., Picton, B. E., Connor, D. W; Howson, C. M. Gilleece, P. and Baguer, M. J. (inpress) Inshore Marine Life of Northern Ireland, HMSO Belfast

Eyles, N. and McCabe, A.M. (1989) The late Devensian (c.22000BP) Irish Sea Basin: the sedimentary record of a collapsed ice sheet margin. *Quaternary Science Reviews* 8, 307–351.

Hamilton, A.C. and Carter, R.W.G. (1983) A mid-Holocene moss bed from eolian dune sands near Articlave, Co. Londonderry. *Irish Naturalists' Journal* 21, 73–75.

Hutchinson, J.N., Prior, D.B. and Stephens, N. (1974) Potentially dangerous surges in an Antrim mudslide. *Quarterly Journal of Engineering Geology* 7, 363–376.

Hydraulics Research Station (1957) *The River Bann Mouth, Northern Ireland.* Report No. 557.

McCabe, A.M. and Eyles, N. (1988) Sedimentology of an ice-contact delta, Carey Valley, Northern Ireland. *Sedimentary Geology* 39, 1–14.

McGreevy, J.P. (1985) A preliminary scanning electron microscope study of honeycomb weathering of sandstone in a coastal environment. *Earth Surface Processes and Landforms*, 10, 509–518.

McMillan, N.F. (1935) Locally extinct marine mollusca at Portstewart. *Journal of Conchology*, 20, 117–126.

McTaggart, H. and Scott, J. (1966) *Coast Protection in Northern Ireland*, Northern Ireland Ministry of Finance, 50pp.

Mitchell, G.F. (1971) The Larnian Culture: a minimal view. *Proceedings of the Prehistoric Society* 38, 274–283.

Pollard, H.J. (1989) Patterns in Irish tourism. In, *Ireland: a Contemporary Geographical Perspective* (Eds. R.W.G. Carter and A.J. Parker) Routledge, London, 301–333.

Preston, J. (1981) Tertiary igneous activity. In, *A Geology of Ireland* (Ed. C.H. Holland) Scottish Academic Press, Edinburgh, 213–223.

Prior, D.B. (1966) Late-glacial and post-glacial shorelines in northeast Antrim. *Irish Geography* 5, 173–187.

Prior, D.B., Stephens, N. and Archer, D.R. (1968)

Composite mudflows on the Antrim coast of north-east Ireland, *Geografiska Annaler*, 50A, 65–78.

Prior, D.B., Holland, S.C. and Cruickshank, M.M. (1981) A preliminary report on late Devensian and early Flandrian deposits at Carnlough, Co. Antrim, *Irish Geography*, 14, 75–84.

Rea, D. (1981) *Decision making in coastal protection in Northern Ireland.* Unpublished M.Sc Thesis, The New University of Ulster, 132pp.

Shaw, J. (1985) The morphodynamics of an Atlantic coast embayment: Runkerry Strand, *Irish Geography* 18, 50–58.

Stephens, N. and Synge, F.M. (1965) Late-Pleistocene shorelines and drift limits in north Donegal. *Proceedings of the Royal Irish Academy*, 65B, 131–153.

Wilcock, F.A. and Carter, R.W.G. (1977) An environmental approach to the restoration of badly eroded sand dunes. *Biological Conservation* 11, 279–291.

Wilson, P. (1987) Soil formation on coastal beach and dune sands at Magilligan Point nature reserve, Co. Londonderry. *Irish Geography* 20, 43–49.

Wilson, P. and Farrington, O. (1989) Radiocarbon dating of the Magilligan Foreland. *Proceedings of the Royal Irish Academy* 89B, 1–23.

INDEX

Antrim Coast Road (A2) 39, 42
Areas of outstanding natural beauty 3, 9
Areas of special control 9
Areas of special scientific interest 9

Ballintoy 29–30
Ballycastle 1, 5, 7, 31–33
Ballygalley 6, 42
Bann Mouth/Estuary 5, 9, 14–16
Bann Valley 4
Boheeshane Bay 30–31

Carnlough 5, 6, 40–41
Castlerock 5, 6, 12, 13, 15
Cliffs 16, 20–21, 24–25, 27–28, 30, 34, 37
Climatic change 11
Coastal erosion 11, 18, 23, 33, 34–35, 36
Coleraine 15, 19
Crown Estate Comissioners 3, 36
Cushendall 1, 36–37
Cushendun 9, 34–36

Department of The Environment (NI) 1, 9, 44
Dredging 15–16
Dunes 10–11, 12, 16, 18–20, 24, 28–29, 37

Fair Head 34

Geology 4–5, 20, 24, 27, 29
Giant's Causeway 3, 6, 9, 22–28
Glaciations 4, 27, 31
Glenarm 6, 40–42
Glens of Antrim 1, 4
Golf Courses 12, 18, 19, 37

Landslips 22–23, 38–39
Larne 8, 42–43
Longshore Currents 7, 8
Lough Foyle 3, 5, 6, 7, 12

Magilligan 3, 7, 8, 10–12, 28
Management 7, 23, 36, 44–45
Motor-cyclists 24
Murlough Bay 3, 9, 34

National Trust 3, 9, 14, 29, 36, 44

Portballintrae 6, 21–24
Portrush 1, 4, 5, 7, 8, 16–20, 28
Portstewart 1, 3, 5, 6, 12–16, 28

Queen's University 42

Raised beaches 5, 27–28, 37
Rathlin Island 30
Rip currents 8, 24, 28
Rivers 6, 9, 15, 24, 31, 34, 38
Runkerry (Bushfoot) 7, 24

Sand removal from beaches 21, 28, 33, 35, 36, 39, 41, 44
Sea-level change 5, 6, 10, 42, 44
Sediments 6, 23–24, 29, 42
Shore protection 16, 19, 23, 35, 36, 37, 40–41, 44
Shore platforms 6, 16

Tidal 'Sundial' 30
Tides 8, 29, 30–31
Tourism 1, 3, 16, 24

University of Ulster 1, 29

Vegetation 11, 12, 37

Waterfoot/Red Bay 6, 37–38
Waves 6–8, 16, 39
Weathering 33–34
White Park Bay 3, 28–29

Printed in the United Kingdom for HMSO

Dd. 8245837   C.8   55-8916   1/91